Dangerous Australians

The complete guide to Australia's most deadly creatures

Compiled by the editors and writers of *The Living Australia* magazine

BAY BOOKS
Sydney and London

• DANGEROUS AUSTRALIANS •

First published 1985 by Bay Books
61–69 Anzac Parade Kensington
New South Wales 2033
Publisher: George Barber
© Bay Books 1985
National Library of Australia Card Number
and ISBN 0 85835 821 2
Printed in Singapore
by Toppan Printing Co.

contents

FOREWORD

by

Ben Cropp

B. Cropp

Australia is a beautiful country, and we love the land, the surf, and the tropical waters of our Great Barrier Reef. But, our enjoyment of this land and sea is threatened by many deadly animals.

In our northern waters we have the box jellyfish, believed to be the most toxic creature known to man. On land, the fierce snake is now recognised as the most venomous land snake in the world.

We have been brought up to believe through imported Westerns and jungle films, that a bite from the rattlesnake or the cobra means almost certain death. It's true that the cobra does kill some ten thousand people each year in India, but our snakes are much worse. We have nineteen snake species which are more venomous than the rattlesnake, and eleven species which have a venom more toxic than the cobra.

When you read these statistics, and see the long list of other dangerous creatures in this book, you may well wonder why you should venture into the sea or the bush at all. Remember that far more people die from drowning or bush accidents than the combined efforts of all these dangerous creatures.

I've survived 35 years of underwater exploration without any serious injury. And, on many occasions I've increased the risks a hundred fold by pushing certain animals into an aggressive or hungry mode just to capture the action on film. Perhaps these creatures are not all that bad. They merely possess the facility to do you great harm — and rarely use it on man unless provoked into defence.

I've always believed that most shark attacks are a mistake on the shark's part. The kicking legs of a swimmer can emulate a struggling, helpless fish or seal. In most cases the shark mouths or tastes the victim. That action and the victim's struggling is sufficient to cause a major injury. It's extremely rare for a shark to actually eat a human victim. Perhaps that is of little consolation to the 135 people who have already died from sharks in Australia.

The Deadly Australians

Quite recently I produced a TV Special called *The Deadly Australians*, which, like this book, looked at all the 'nasties' which live in the sea and on the land. I drew on my own 35 years of underwater activities to cover the list of dangerous marine creatures. With the land snakes and the spiders, I found I enjoyed the challenge of facing the creatures I once abhorred, and learning their behaviour and how they hunt for food. The more we learn about a nasty creature, the less horrifying it becomes.

Our knowledge of these creatures' habits is important if we wish to reduce the incidence of bites and fatalities. Education, in layman's terms, is what this book is about.

Over the past five years I've filmed four separate TV documentaries on our dangerous creatures. The first was on tiger sharks feeding, the second on the highly venomous box jellyfish, the third on crocodiles, and then all the dangerous creatures grouped under *The Deadly Australians*.

Years without injury

In all those years, working full time among the most dangerous of all creatures and handling some of them many times over, none of my team were injured. That says something for these creatures. Of course, our encounters were backed up by lots of experience, care, and very calculated risks.

I did actually sustain one injury — but it was self-inflicted. My wife Lynn placed the tentacles of a box jellyfish on both my arms and we waited one minute before pouring methylated spirits over one arm and household vinegar on the other. It was an experiment in the early days of box jellyfish research, when some experts relied on metho to treat stingers and others newly advocated the use of vinegar. Since I was handling box jellyfish every day, suffering some minor stings, I wanted to be sure which remedy to use if I did receive a major sting.

The result of my experiment was a lot of pain in both arms. Vinegar did win however, successfully neutralising the unfired nematocysts. The methylated spirits gave me a secondary sting when it triggered off those unfired stinging cells.

Of all the creatures mentioned in this book, the behaviour of the box jellyfish is the least known. My underwater research has revealed the predators of the box jellyfish. Now I'm studying their migratory habits in the hope of determining safe periods for swimming in the summer stinger season.

Calculated feeders

Out on the Barrier Reef, I filmed the way tiger sharks feed. A 500 kilogram black marlin carcass attracted about ten tigers right up behind my boat. We saw that they were unhurried, calculated feeders, actually taking turns to feed. The largest tiger dominated, often pushing in for more turns than the others.

Often the sharks were only a metre from my camera, and it was amazing to watch and learn exactly how they feed. There were no quick bites. The tiger lunged into the fish carcass with

FOREWORD

jaws agape and locked on. He pushed and bit and pushed until the maximum amount of meat was in his jaws, then he closed those massive jaws and twisted and wrenched a huge mouthful from the marlin.

This is not what sharks do to humans. They seem to make that first lunge and then retreat. Perhaps we are not so tasty after all.

Filming the crocodiles was the most challenging. We lay in a hide to film unique footage on the female making her nest, and the same female opening her nest 80 days later to release her babies.

Caring mothers

One nesting female almost had us. They are at their worst behaviour when guarding the nest. At Edward River in the Gulf, I was filming Don Morris, the soundman, checking a nest to see if the croc had laid. She came out of her mud wallow and charged us. We ran fast, very fast indeed for the croc did not catch us. My soundman tumbled over and broke the microphone. I had left my camera running and it showed everything — a brief steady shot of the charging croc, and very shaky scenes of the sky, the bush, and scurrying feet.

Experience did actually help us in this case. We knew that if a croc charged, it was best to run until the croc stopped; they are very territorial and will not chase you too far.

The great crocodile, a descendant of the dinosaur, is making a rapid comeback from the edge of extinction. It's returning to old river haunts alongside man's expanding development, creating a conflict between man and the croc. Since it appears to threaten our enjoyment of the waterways, few people show concern for the crocodile's right to live.

Education is important through films and books such as this one. We must understand the crocodile's role and be prepared to share the rivers with this big and ancient and grotesquely magnificent creature.

The chapter on first aid is a must to read, for your knowledge on this may save lives. Do keep in touch with modern first aid methods for they constantly change as our knowledge and science improves.

Methylated spirits is "out" and vinegar is "in" as the remedy today for all marine stingers. The old tourniquet and "cut and suck" method is thankfully out for snake bites. Now it is simply the use of a broad compressive bandage and the injection of an antivenom. This new treatment truly saves lives — so much so that the death rate from snake bite in Australia has fallen from 14 to only one per year.

Today, your first aid kit is very simple. A bottle of vinegar, a compressive bandage, and a knowledge of expired air resuscitation will save most lives.

Of course, avoiding an attack should always be your first concern. The knowledge imparted in this book on all our dangerous creatures will help you achieve this.

Ben Cropp

Australia's 'Top Ten' Potential Killers

Australia has a reputation for possessing the most dangerous creatures in the world — and who could argue with such a reputation after reading the following chapter? Every one of the following creatures is capable of inflicting a fatal bite or sting. However, given the opportunity, most will try to avoid contact with humans. Although they have a great potential for threatening human life, rarely is this potential realised.

FUNNEL-WEB SPIDER

The world's deadliest spider

A female funnel-web in the 'fangs up' stance. Funnel-webs must raise their bodies before striking, as their fangs are limited to downward movement.

The funnel-web was recognised as extremely dangerous many years ago, and since then stories enhancing its reputation have been spread worldwide. For the most part, fiction seems to have replaced fact, but there is no disputing that this is the deadliest spider in the world.

The facts as they are known today: funnel-webs cannot leap or jump on you from trees, nor will they deliberately seek out a human victim; invenomation by a funnel-web will not cause instantaneous death, although pain is felt immediately; the bad news is, funnel-webs are highly resistant to spray pesticides.

To many people spiders are dangerous animals, to be avoided at all costs and killed whenever possible. It is certainly true that most spiders are venomous but in only very few species is the venom powerful enough to affect

ANT K. Atkinson

human beings or the fangs which inject it long enough to pierce human skin. The venom spiders inject paralyses or kills their prey and also helps to release the juices the spider feeds on. However, most spiders are timid and will not bite even if handled. They perform a useful task in houses and gardens, catching many insects regarded as pests.

At home in suburbia

The funnel-web has proved itself quite adaptable, and has happily taken up residence in suburban gardens. It is especially fond of hiding under houses, in a forgotten corner of an old shed or amongst a pile of rubbish. Wet weather seems to arouse them, possibly because their homes become flooded. Funnel-webs are basically insectivorous, but they also feed on prey as large as lizards and frogs.

Funnel-webs and trapdoor spiders are Mygalomorphs, the most primitive of all spiders. They are medium to large, solidly-built spiders, brown to black in colour. Mygalomorphs are characterised by their long fangs which move vertically downward so that the spider must rear up to strike.

Funnel-web spiders occur in many parts of the world, but the genus *Atrax* is found only in Australia, where nine species (it is estimated that there are some 40 species in Australia) have been described. They range from southeastern Queensland through New South Wales into Victoria and Tasmania and west to the Mount Lofty Ranges of South Australia. They are common in moist coastal and mountain localities, but some species have extended their range to drier areas such as the western slopes of the Great Dividing Range, and Flinders Range in South Australia.

The most feared of the funnel-webs, the **Sydney funnel-web** was for many years thought to be confined to the sandstone area around Sydney. It has now been identified in southeastern Victoria and is most common in central New South Wales from Newcastle south to Nowra and as far west as Lithgow.

Males take two or three years to reach sexual maturity, but then survive only six to eight months. Females mature in three to four years and live at least five years. Females maintain permanent retreats which they progressively enlarge, and here they keep and guard their egg sacs.

Tree dweller

The **tree funnel-web** or **northern funnel-web**, *A. formidabilis*, is found from southeastern Queensland through the mountainous regions of northern New South Wales, the Hunter River Valley forming its southernmost limit. The largest of the funnel-webs, it reaches 5 centimetres in body length and builds its bark-shrouded retreat on tree trunks as high as 30

ANT/K. Atkinson

The female Sydney funnel-web, *Atrax robustus*.

The male Sydney funnel-web, *Atrax robustus*.

The rearing motion of the funnel-web (above) is often thought to be a sign of aggression, however the stance is usually only taken if the spider is provoked. The Blue Mountains funnel-web (below) is just as toxic as its Sydney counterpart, but because it occupies a less populated area, its reputation is not as great.

Bay Picture Library

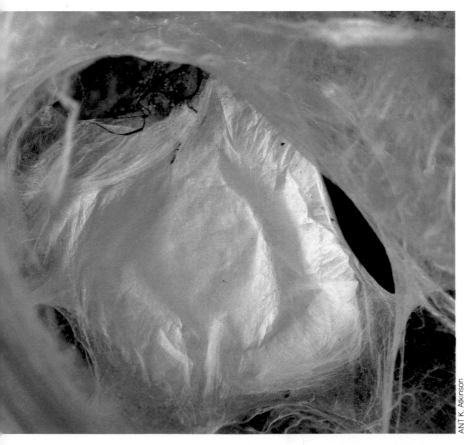

metres above the ground. The numerous insects which live on and under the bark or use tree trunks as routes to food sources in the canopy above provide much of the food supply for these and other tree-dwelling spiders, but lizards and frogs are also eaten.

One tree-dwelling species, as yet unnamed, is common in the Sydney region from the southern suburbs north to Gosford and is associated with rough-barked trees such as paperbark (*Melaleuca*), banksia, she-oak and swamp oak (*Casuarina*) and some eucalypts. Several other tree-dwelling funnel-webs have been found but remain undescribed.

The distribution of the **Blue Mountain funnel-web**, *A. versutus*, is self-evident, but occasional specimens have been taken as far east as Sydney and as far west as Orange. **A. modesta** has been found near Melbourne and in Victoria's Grampian Mountains, and an undescribed species has been recorded in the alpine regions of the Brindabella Range and

How dangerous is the Sydney funnel-web?

When irritated, both males and females exude a poison droplet from the tips of their fangs. The venom of the female, which grows to 4 centimetres, is far less toxic than that of the male, which is only about 2.5 centimetres in body length but has longer legs than the female.

Contact between people and the Sydney funnel-web is most likely during the summer-autumn breeding season when males venture forth in search of a female. In these nocturnal excursions they may blunder inadvertently into houses and garages, being quite capable of climbing up walls and through windows as well as through gaps between doors and floors.

Funnel-web bites cause severe pain at the site of injection of the poison and quickly spreads throughout the body. Excessive sweating, salivation and vomiting may occur, and blood pressure may rise rapidly with coma or respiratory obstruction following occasionally. All funnel-webs should be regarded as potentially dangerous and capable of causing severe illness, although only the male is known to have caused deaths — over thirteen in the past seventy years.

Because of the publicity Sydney-siders are especially conscious of the dangers of the Sydney funnel-web, but the Blue Mountains funnel-web is just as toxic, if not more toxic than the Sydney species. In the case of the Blue Mountains funnel-web the male and female appear to be equally dangerous.

According to Dr Merlin Howden of Macquarie University in Sydney the funnel-web is a spider who does not seek trouble and will only become aggressive if cornered or irritated. Dr Merlin and his associates were responsible for much of the work that finally culminated in finding a successful antivenom for the funnel-web in 1980. Provided correct first aid is given, and the casualty reaches hospital quickly, he or she should suffer no lasting ill effects.

Funnel-web bites should be treated by applying a broad pressure bandage not a tourniquet, immobilising the limb and keeping the patient quiet. Medical assistance must be sought as soon as possible.

The tree funnel-web, *Atrax formidabilis* (opposite top) occurs in mountainous areas from south-east Queensland to the Hunter River in New South Wales. A close-up of the fangs of the female funnel-web (opposite centre). The silken egg case of the funnel-web (opposite bottom). The nest or burrow of the funnel-web is, as its name suggests, funnel-shaped (below). A funnel-web claims another victim, this time a skink (bottom).

The female tree funnel-web, *Atrax formidabilis*.

other high mountains in New South Wales where it hibernates in a silken tube under logs and stones beneath the snow. Two *Atrax* species occur in the highlands of Tasmania.

Confusion about webs

The webs of these spiders vary in both placement and appearance according to species. Much confusion has arisen because of the common name, as the surface webs covering burrows or other hollows do not look at all like funnels. The web of the ground-dwelling Sydney funnel-web consists of a flat, purse-like chamber of white silk lying on the ground surface under a log, rock or the like. There are usually two short entrance tubes leading into this chamber, the whole forming a Y-shaped configuration. This is guyed out to surrounding vegetation by numerous silk threads, the only part of an undisturbed retreat that is visible. Prey is taken at the edge of the web, when guy lines convey vibrations set up by the approach of potential victims.

> **'Prey is taken at the edge of the web.'**

'... living in Australia for millions of years, unceremoniously killing its victims with its highly toxic venom.'

Enough venom to kill 250 000 mice

FIERCE SNAKE

ANT C&R Wilson

There is no need to beat around the bush when classifying this snake — it is the most dangerous of all Australian snakes. The only bit of good news is that humans and the fierce snake rarely cross paths.

Infamy came belatedly for this highly dangerous snake: until 1975 there were no live specimens collected of the fierce or small-scaled snake, *Oxyuranus microlepidotus*. And yet, it must have been living in Australia for millions of years, unceremoniously killing its victims with its highly toxic venom.

The fierce snake lives up perfectly to its formidable name: its average venom yield is 44 milligrams though up to 110 milligrams have been recorded. The venom is extremely toxic, the most toxic of all land snakes in the world: a full dose of its venom is enough to kill a quarter of a million mice. A rat bitten by the fierce snake would die within a few seconds, its nervous system and heart instantly paralysed.

Needless to say, the venom is also dangerous for humans; despite an increasing number of specimens now available for milking, the taipan's antivenene is normally used to neutralise the toxin.

Fortunately for humans, the fierce snake lives off the beaten track, in isolated patches over a large area of southwestern Queensland, western New South Wales and adjacent parts of South Australia and the Northern Territory; most specimens have been collected from near the channel systems of Cooper Creek and the Diamantina River.

Because of its late 'discovery', few facts are known about this snake's habits. In western Queensland it feeds on the plague rat and often lives in underground burrows the rats have excavated. In droughts the snake shelters in deep cracks of the ashy downs and may survive long periods of intense heat without food or water.

In appearance the fierce snake is similar to the taipan: the body is deep brown above and the head is usually a glossy black. The average length of recently captured specimens is 1.7 metres. The scales are smooth and at mid-body there are 23 rows●

Distribution

To date this snake, the fierce snake, has been found to have the most toxic venom of any animal. Related to the taipan, it was only recently 'discovered' and there are many questions yet to be answered about the habits and preferences of this formidable creature.

TAIPANS

Rapid-fire bite

A.N.T Fred Parker

A.N.T S Wilson

The youngest taipan in the family (above right) looks around for his or her first victim.

The taipan (above) was for many years believed to be the world's most deadly snake; it has just been replaced by its relative, the fierce snake.

> **'Snakes can literally commit accidental suicide.'**

Every layman, terrified of snake bite, must have wondered occasionally whether snakes themselves are immune to their own poison. The verdict: snakes can literally commit accidental suicide.

Leading Australian naturalist and snake expert Eric Worrell has observed a taipan bite itself on the back. It died within minutes, probably because the venom entered a vital area.

The bad news is that taipans are equally deadly for humans and are, in fact, the second-most dangerous snake you can find in the Australian bush. So stop searching for them, unless you are in the business of collecting venom.

A member of the highly venomous family Elapidae, the taipan — *Oxyuranus scutellatus* — are most often found in wet forests. They can be seen all over northern Australia and Queensland and even in western parts of New South Wales up to the junction of the Murray and Darling rivers. As they live on the ground, they blend easily into their surroundings: the brown colour, creamy or yellow belly spotted with orange provide a perfect camouflage.

And they need it, too: taipans, like all other snakes, have myriad natural enemies. Eagles, kookaburras, butcherbirds, magpies, crows, foxes and other snakes attack them wihout the slightest hesitation. Fires also decimate them. For some mysterious reason, most snakes make little effort to escape bushfires and often perish in large numbers.

Against all hazards, the taipan relies on its murderous venom which is highly neurotoxic and coagulant. It uses this weapon when hunting for food — mainly small mammals such as mice, rats, small bandicoots, lizards and birds — or, to defend itself. The taipan slides quietly through the grass, finding its prey by scent then flinging itself at its victim. One or several rapid-fire bites follow — and the next meal is just about ready.

Taipans, like other venomous snakes, use their poison sparingly. As they instinctively don't regard man as a prey, they may strike and hit a human foot — without releasing any venom at all.

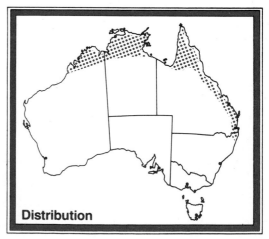

Distribution

Taipan, *Oxyuranus scutellatus*.

A retiring taipan

Actually, contrary to myths and widespread fears, taipans are shy, preferring to escape from human proximity. Worrell has estimated that some 80 per cent of all snake attacks occur when people try to catch or kill a snake and the rest when somebody, accidentally, steps on them in the bush. And as taipans often grow to more than three metres in length, they are not all that hard to detect in the bush — especially if you bear in mind their possible presence.

Until about 25 years ago a taipan's venom was often, though not always, fatal to humans. However, thanks to the Commonwealth Serum Laboratories and the people who supply them with taipan venom, an effective antivenene has been developed and is available. Still, the venom can cause severe pains and illness.

Most dangerous Australian snakes bear live young but the taipan lays eggs, up to 30 white, elongated eggs deposited in or under logs, in cracks or crevices in moist places. Hatching takes between 10 and 14 weeks and the new-born are expected to fend for themselves right from the start. Taipans are believed to live for 20 years or longer. ●

Juvenile taipan (above) swallowing a mouse.

It slides stealthily through the grasses and over the logs (below) to find prey. Once found the taipan is merciless.

WHICH BROWN SNAKE IS WHICH?

The eastern brown snake

The mention of brown snakes usually evokes images of the king brown snake, one of Australia's most widespread and most dangerous snakes. But the king brown is really a member of the group commonly, and confusingly, called black snakes. Both groups are extremely dangerous.

The six species of brown snake (family Elapidae, genus *Pseudonaja*) in Australia are very difficult to identify, as each varies widely in colour and pattern. They range from pale brown, russet or grey to dark brown or almost black above some with spots or bands, and cream, yellow, orange or grey below.

The head is indistinct or only slightly distinct from the neck and the body is generally slender and streamlined, varying in maximum length from 50 centimetres in the ringed brown snake, *P. modesta*, to 2.5 metres in the eastern brown snake, *P. textilis*.

Brown snakes have a feeding habit which is most unusual among elapid snakes. When attacking larger prey, in addition to injecting venom, they coil the forebody around the victim and apply constriction in the same way as boas and pythons. They feed largely on lizards and small mammals, although small birds, frogs and other snakes may also be eaten. When small prey are captured, they are held in the mouth until dead or nearly so.

Like all snakes brown snakes ingest food animals whole and have the ability to swallow prey larger than their own heads. The jaws are connected by elastic ligaments which allow this distention. Most prey are swallowed head first to minimise resistance from scales, fur and feathers. When the swallowed animal has moved past the snake's windpipe, the snake moves about,

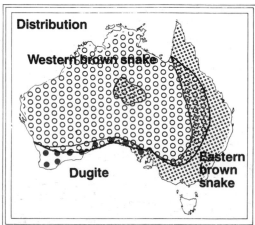

Distribution

Western brown snake

Dugite

Eastern brown snake

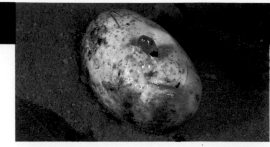

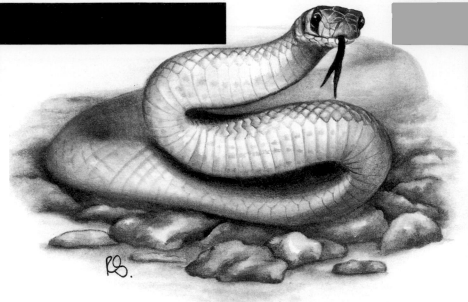

The eastern brown snake (above), *Pseudonaja textilis*.

The young hatching here is a western brown snake or gwardar. There are normally 20 eggs in a clutch and the colours of the young are usually much brighter than those of the adult.

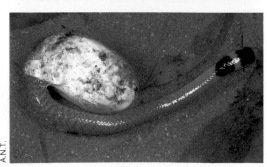

stretching its jaws vigorously until the dislocated bones have resumed their normal alignment.

True brown snakes lay eggs, usually around 20 per clutch. Hatchlings may measure up to 20 centimetres long at birth, according to the species. Colours and patterns are generally much brighter and more distinct in the young, fading with age. Like all snakes, brown snakes slough their skins regularly, more often as they are growing, decreasing in frequency with maturity.

Daylight on the prowl

Brown snakes are mostly diurnal but may also be nocturnal during warm weather and in northern climates. They occupy a range of habitats and are most often found in cracks and crevices, under

southwest. The ringed brown snake lives in the drier areas of all mainland states except Victoria. **Ingram's brown snake,** *P. ingrami,* is known only from the Barkly Tableland of the Northern Territory and far western Queensland, and the **speckled brown snake,** *P. guttata,* from central Queensland and the eastern Northern Territory, the **dugite,** *P. affinis* is restricted to the southwestern corner of Western Australia, extending eastward along a narrow coastal strip to South Australia's Eyre Peninsula.

All brown snakes are dangerous and should be treated with extreme caution or avoided if possible. Anyone bitten by a brown snake should seek medical attention immediately.

Putting the king brown in its place

The king brown or mulga snake, *Pseudechis australis,* belongs to the same genus as the red-bellied black snake. It is found in almost all habitat types and occurs throughout the continent except the southwest corner, most of the South Australian coast, in Victoria and in New South Wales east of the Great Dividing Range.

Its diet and habits are similar to those of the true brown snake except that it bears live young; a litter of twenty-two has been recorded. It is aggressive and unpredictable and it strikes with extreme rapidity, injecting large quantities of venom due to its large size. Although two metres is average, king browns' up to 2.8 metres have been sighted. ●

stones, in or under logs or down rabbit or other burrows.

Swiftly moving animals they prefer to escape if threatened but cornered, they will strike repeatedly or hold on tenaciously. Their venoms are neurotoxic and some contain strong coagulants and blood-destroying properties. Only the **ringed brown snake** is not considered dangerous, due to its small size.

The **eastern brown snake** occurs from Cape York Peninsula to coastal South Australia and perhaps further westward with an isolated population in central Australia. It is also found in New Guinea. The **western brown snake** or **gwardar,** *P. nuchalis,* is found throughout the continent except the extreme east, southeast and

Adult western brown snake (top) and the king brown snake (centre). The king brown is often erroneously placed with the true brown snakes (right).

A.N.T RWG Jenkins

Although their venom is one of the most potent known, tiger snakes have a reputation for ferocity and aggressiveness which may be quite unjustified.

Tiger snakes, which have caused a high proportion of this country's deaths from snakebite, were recorded by zoologist Gerhard Krefft in 1866 as being Australia's most dangerous reptiles. This view persisted until the 1920s, when data of the even more toxic taipan became available, and it is now known that the copperhead, the small rough-scaled snake and the common brown snake are just as deadly.

All these species belong to the family Elapidae, front-fanged venomous snakes which include some of the most dangerous species in the world — African cobras and mambas, Asian cobras and kraits, American coral snakes and the Australian death adders. In fact, the majority of Australian land snakes belongs to this family but the venom of many species is only mildly toxic and not considered dangerous to humans.

The tiger snake's reputation for ferocity may have been based on Krefft's observation of the quite justifiable fear in which the Aboriginals held these reptiles. However, Eric Worrell, who captures and milks tiger snakes of their venom for the production of antivenene, considers them to be 'inoffensive unless aroused'. If cornered or provoked they will assume a striking stance, holding the body in a long, low curve with the neck flattened and swaying, and hissing, while waiting to strike which they may do repeatedly. Tiger snakes are widely distributed in southern Australia from southeastern Queensland to South Australia, in the southwestern corner of

While they are not regarded as aggressive, tiger snakes will attack viciously when provoked. To strike it raises its body in a long, narrow curve, hisses and sways while preparing to strike. The eastern brown (above) has a tendency to puff up his neck cobra-style.

TIGER SNAKES

Deadly swamp denizens

The highly venomous mainland tiger snake.

'They are still found as close to Sydney as Botany Bay.'

Western Australia, in Tasmania and on offshore and Bass Strait islands. Their range extends well inland to swamps such as those along the Lachlan River where shooters hunting wild pig are said to encounter them, and to the high valleys of the Snowy Mountains. Since tiger snakes inhabit the most populated parts of Australia, unlike the taipan and other dangerous snakes, they quite commonly occur near settled areas. They are still found as close to Sydney as the Botany area.

Although tiger snakes frequent a wide range of habitats from comparatively dry rocky areas and coastal dune grasslands to moist eucalypt forests and rainforests, they are most common, and sometimes occur in large colonies, in damp and boggy regions. Here they shelter among

A.N.T S Wilson

Eastern tiger snake, *Notechis scutatus* (top left). Black tigers (above) on King Island are cannibalistic but in the main feed on frogs, small mammals and occasionally mutton bird chicks. The range of an eastern tiger (right) and when the snake attacks, the fangs come at you at an astonishing speed. Black tiger snake, *Notechis ater* (left).

Bay Picture Library

While the stripes on the tiger snake made the choice of its name easy, the name has also given the snake an undeserved reputation for aggressiveness.

A.N.T Peter Krauss

tussocky grasses, under logs or in holes in the ground, foraging during the day and sometimes on warm summer nights for frogs, lizards, small mammals and, occasionally, fish.

Although the classification of tiger snakes has been disputed, it is now generally agreed that there are two species — the eastern or mainland tiger snake, *Notechis scutatus*, and the black tiger snake, *N. ater* — and a number of distinct geographical races.

The mainland tiger snake is variable in colour, ranging from light grey through olive, brown and reddish to a dark blackish-brown above, with a cream, yellow, olive green or grey belly. Narrow light crossbands may be present on the back. It is found from southeastern Queensland through eastern and southern New South Wales, across most of Victoria and into South Australia. The black tiger snake, as its name implies, is black or very dark brown with a light to dark grey belly. Faint lighter or darker crossbands may be visible, especially in juveniles. It occurs in Tasmania and the Bass Strait Islands; the Flinders Range, Eyre Peninsula and offshore islands in South Australia; and in southwestern Western Australia.

Up to 100 in litter

Both species are stout-bodied snakes, seldom longer than 1.5 metres, but the race found on several Bass Strait islands, the Chappell Island tiger snake, is known to reach 2.5 metres in length. It lives in muttonbird burrows, feeding on chicks in the breeding season and posing a hazard to muttonbird hunters. Like Krefft's tiger snake, which is jet black with a grey belly and occurs in the Flinders Range in South Australia, it is unusual in occupying a very dry habitat.

Tiger snakes are ovoviviparous, producing live young from soft-shelled eggs incubated inside the female. A normal litter is about 30, but from 17 to over 100 young have been recorded. The breeding season is from October to December and gestation takes about fourteen weeks, birth occurring in late autumn to early winter.

Venom and antivenene

Experiments with the venom of tiger snakes were carried out as early as 1876 (by the Snake Bite Committee of the Medical Society of Victoria) and there has been more research on this venom than of any other Australian snakes. There is considerable variation in the quantity and potency of venom from the various forms of tiger snake but all are dangerous to humans. It is both coagulant and neurotoxic in its action, causing paralysis and respiratory failure and sometimes impaired vision or even blindness.

The antivenene developed for tiger snake venom was the first to be made in Australia and has been produced commercially by the Commonwealth Serum Laboratories since 1928. It is also used against the venom of copperheads, brown and black snakes, mulga snakes, and a variety of Indian and American snakes. ●

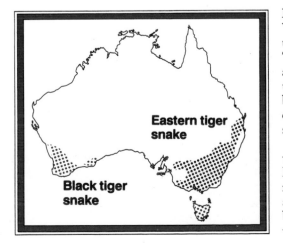

Eastern tiger snake

Black tiger snake

SEA SNAKES

Highly dangerous and capable of causing death to man, the venom of a sea snake has been rated as 10 times more toxic than that of a cobra. Although they breathe air, sea snakes have the remarkable ability to stay submerged for up to eight hours.

Often confused with eels, sea snakes belong to the family Hydrophilidae and are common in the warm, tropical seas of northern Australia where they are often sighted by skin divers and fishermen.

There are at least 30 species of sea snakes in Australia and they range through Queensland coastal and estuarine waters, northward through Torres Strait and into tropical Western Australia and southwards through New South Wales coastal regions into central Victoria. There have also been isolated sightings as far south as Tasmania.

One of the commonest and largest of the Queensland species is the elegant sea snake, *Hydrophis elegans* which grows to over two metres long. Fishermen working inshore coastal waters, estuaries and lakes will often capture sea snakes in their trawl nets. They are identified by their valvular nostrils and flattened, paddle like tail.

The yellow-bellied sea snake, *Pelamis platurus* which is another common species has a clear division between its black back and yellow sides and belly. Its tail is creamish yellow with large, dark blotches and its average length is less than one metre. The young of sea snakes are born alive at sea except those of the banded sea snake, *Laticauda colubrine* which comes ashore to lay up to 20 eggs.

Submerged for hours

Excellent swimmers, sea snakes frequently dive to considerable depths in search of fish and eels which are their favourite diet. They can remain submerged for hours due to their ability to store air in their right lung which is very long and extends to the base of the tail.

Some species have been observed floating on the surface of the water where they will quickly devour any inquisitive fish which rises to inves-

Bay Picture Library

The head of the sea snake (top) showing the traditional mottled skin of reptiles and its forked tongue. Three milligrams of venom is potent enough to cause death. Sea snake making its way through the corals (above).

❛ Although only small amounts of venom are produced, it is extremely toxic. ❜

Common in Queensland's coral reef waters, the sea snake (right) is an excellent swimmer. The banded sea snake (top right) comes ashore on islands to lay its eggs. The yellow-bellied sea snake is often washed ashore after a storm or caught in trawl nets.

ANT — Fred Parker

A.N.T. John Cann

tigate it. Sea snakes shed their skin as often as every two weeks and this is done probably as a means of preventing a build up of marine growth.

A small dose of venom can cause death

The fangs of sea snakes are small, fixed and situated near the front of the mouth. Although only small amounts of venom are produced, it is, in most cases extremely toxic: a dose as low as two to three milligrams is potent enough to cause death in humans. Fortunately not all bites inject large amounts of toxin and are often times just a defensive bite when disturbed.

Sea snakes should never be picked up except by those experienced at doing so. Care should be taken by those handling fishing nets in tropical waters, especially at night. Many specimens have been taken in the nets of prawn trawlers working the Gulf of Carpentaria. Some fishermen have been bitten by accidentally grasping a sea snake lying in the folds of a net or wrapped about cordage.

Despite colourful tales by skin divers, sea snakes are shy and are not aggressive if left alone. They only bite if touched or molested. The symptoms of a bite include a generalised aching that leads to weakness and paralysis, lockjaw, muscular twitchings and spasm, respiratory distress which culminates in cardiac failure, convulsions and coma.

Antivenene is available

An antivenom made in Australia against the venom of the beaked sea snake combined with tiger snake antivenom has been found to neutralise all the important sea snake venoms. However, before the victim is hospitalised, first aid treatment can be vital to survival.

The Commonwealth Serum Laboratories recommends these first aid measures. First, all unnecessary movement must be avoided by the victim. Immediately apply a broad pressure bandage over the site of the bite and wrap it around the limb. A crepe bandage is most suitable but if it's necessary to improvise, strips of towelling, bedding or other cloth is useful. The limb should be kept as still as possible by applying a splint; a branch, fishing rod or any other rigid object at hand can be used.

In the case of a bite on the leg, the bandage should be bound firmly to as much of the leg as possible. With bites on the hand or forearm, the limb should be splinted to the elbow and the arm placed in a sling. Both the pressure bandage and the splint should be left in place until removed by a medical practitioner.

Serious poisoning occurs in only about one in four cases of sea snake bite. Where the victim has been badly affected, it may be necessary to give artificial respiration if medical assistance is delayed.

Bay Picture Library

Family reunion of saltwater crocodiles. The species have survived some 180 million turbulent years.

A VORACIOUS MAN-EATER

THE SALTWATER CROCODILE

Highly intelligent with few natural enemies, the saltwater crocodile, *Crocodylus porosus*, of Australia's northern tropical waters is an aggressive predator, highly dangerous to man. It is one of two species in the world which are known to attack man without provocation. The other is the African Nile crocodile, *C. niloticus*.

Crocodiles are among the most ancient of the earth's creatures, having survived substantially unchanged for more than 180 million years. They evolved from prehistoric reptilian lifeforms that also gave rise to dinosaurs, pterosaurs and other animals long since extinct. There are 20 or so different crocodile species throughout the world, all of which are closely related to alligators, caimans and a single species of gavial.

Tropical habitat

Crocodiles and their relatives are generally restricted to tropical and subtropical regions and are confined to the north and northeastern coasts of the Australian continent. The saltwater crocodile and the freshwater species, *C. johnstoni,* are readily distinguishable by the length and shape of their snouts: very long and slim in the freshwater species, broader and blunter in the 'salties'. 'Freshies' are also much smaller, growing to no more than about 2.5 metres whereas saltwater crocodiles are more than three times this size.

Strong, swishing tail

Although Australia's freshwater crocodile is an endemic species, studies here have centred largely on the saltwater crocodile. Like all crocodilians the estuarine crocodile is well adapted for its semi-aquatic life. The rear feet are webbed and the muscular tail, which is flattened like a paddle, swishes from side to side to propel the animal through the water. The eyes and nostrils are on top of the head and the nose can be closed off by flaps of skin to prevent water entering the respiratory system. The teeth may number from

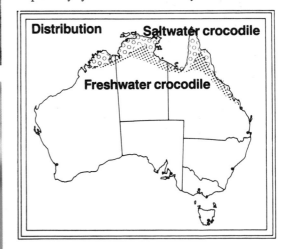

No seasoned bushman would be deceived by the docile look on this crocodile's face.

40 to 60 and are used for grasping rather than chewing. Food is swallowed whole or in chunks.

The crocodile's diet changes markedly during its lifecycle. Hatchlings eat small fish when they can catch them, other less agile aquatic creatures, and insects. They are in turn eaten by large fish, by pelicans, ibises and other waterbirds and, not insignificantly, by larger crocodiles. Juveniles eat larger fish and small birds and mammals, and are themselves preyed on by sharks and sometimes larger crocodiles.

Adult crocodiles eat anything that comes too close: fish, birds, and mammals of any size that venture near the water's edge. They sometimes attack small boats but this is usually interpreted as territorial aggression rather than attempted predation.

Eggs incubated by the sun

In Australia, saltwater crocodiles breed during the summer wet season. On the riverbank, the female builds a mound of vegetation near the top of which she deposits 70 or more eggs which are then covered with more vegetation. The eggs are incubated by the heat of the sun coupled with heat produced by decomposition of the heaped vegetation. The mound is guarded by the female until the hatching young call out, at which time she helps them escape by digging into the nest. The mounds are not always built well above the high water mark and many eggs are lost through flooding, particularly those near the bottom of the pile.

100 year life span

The mother shepherds her newly hatched young into the water and guards them for several weeks. This behaviour is unique among reptiles, which normally take no further interest in their eggs once they are laid. The newborn crocodiles are about 25 centimetres long but grow rapidly until they reach sexual maturity at eight or ten years of age when about three metres long. Thereafter the growth rate slows with age. Crocodiles may live for more than 100 years.

Adult males are extremely territorial and will only tolerate the presence of juveniles considerably smaller than themselves. Once too large, these young are forced away and travel along the coast until they find a suitable habitat. Some swim out to sea and, although many fall prey to sharks, saltwater crocodiles have been known to reach destinations hundreds of kilometres across the ocean from the nearest known population.

Man as predator: the need for conservation

Crocodilians have been hunted from earliest times. Their flesh and eggs are highly prized as food by many indigenous peoples including the Australian Aboriginals. Parts of the body such as the teeth and entrails have traditionally been used as charms or medicinal cures in many societies, as the Venetian traveller Marco Polo noted during his eastern journeys in the thirteenth century. Above all, the hides of these creatures, particularly the soft belly skin, are valuable as a fine leather. Distinctively patterned

Saltwater crocodile

Freshwater crocodile

Crocodiles hatching at Port Moresby Experimental Farm (top) and a cross-section of an egg. Harmless freshwater species (above) are fairly common in northern Australia. Saltwater crocs (right) attain a greater length.

crocodile skin commands high prices when manufactured into handbags, shoes, belts, briefcases and other leather goods.

The use of simple weapons at close range by primitive peoples rarely endangered the survival of the species. Modern hunters, on the other hand, have the advantage of guns and motorised aluminium boats which allows them to remain at a relatively safe distance. Crocodiles are disadvantaged by having a highly reflective covering (tapetum) over their eyes which glows red in a spotlight, making them easy to detect at night. The upper surface of the body is thick and tough, strengthened by close-set bony plates just beneath it which are responsible for the ability of crocodiles to deflect a powerful blow or even a bullet. However, this is insufficient protection against man and his technology. Crocodile populations in Australia and elsewhere have reached dangerously low levels. ●

'Crocodile populations in Australia and elsewhere have reached dangerously low levels.'

A bitter and heated battle

Australia's crocodiles became fully protected in 1972 when Queensland passed protective legislation similar to that already in force in Western Australia and the Northern Territory. In the same year an intensive research program was undertaken by the government of the Northern Territory and the University of Sydney's School of Physics to monitor crocodile populations and learn more about their habits and lifecycles. This study provided enormous insight into the behaviour and ecological needs of crocodiles, and studies are still being carried out by the university research team.

Australia's saltwater crocodile is presently included on Appendix 1 of the Endangered Species List of the International Union for the Conservation of Nature (IUCN). This means that no listed animal taken from the wild may be killed or its products put to commercial use, although captives may be exhibited; any animal sold must have been born of parents which bred in captivity. In line with similar activities elsewhere in the world, a crocodile farm is operating quite successfully under these conditions at Edward River on Cape York Peninsula, and the government of the Northern Territory recently established a $640 000 crocodile ranch near Darwin which is stocked mainly with animals culled from rivers near populated areas where they are a danger to people.

Commercial interests would like to raise and market animals taken from the wild, which is permissible with animals listed on IUCN's Appendix 2, and much effort has been spent in trying to effect a change of listing. Those favouring the change argue that since protection was instituted crocodile populations have increased to an extent that the animals are no longer in danger of extinction. Scientists who are continuing to monitor the animals in their habitat, however, are convinced that any commercial exploitation of animals from the wild would again place saltwater crocodiles in grave danger of extinction in some or all of their Australian habitats.

The battle has become heated and bitter. It is to be hoped that a solution will be found which will ensure the survival of a species that has existed on this planet for nearly 200 million years. ●

THE BOX JELLYFISH

The feared box jellyfish or sea wasp of northern Australian waters has caused 70 deaths since 1900. An adult specimen with its long, trailing tentacles contains enough venom to kill at least three men.

Although it has an innocuous appearance of a flimsy, transparent head and a cluster of long, trailing tentacles, the box jellyfish, *Chironex fleckeri* or sea wasp is arguably the most poisonous of all animals. It has claimed the lives of many swimmers in northern Queensland waters and most children have died within minutes of being stung.

The box jellyfish can be found in coastal waters, creeks and rivers north from 22° south which is the latitude in the vicinity of Mackay, Queensland. Its range is from the north Queensland coast into the Northern Territory and around the northern coastline of Western Australia.

It is most prevalent during the summer months from November to mid-March although stings and deaths have been reported at other times of the year. A hazard to both swimmers and fishermen, the box jellyfish is mostly seen on days when the water is calm. They move into the shallow waters of creeks and rivers in search of prawns which are their main diet. Due to the summer wet season, these waterways are often flooded and muddy making it difficult to see the box jellyfish before its too late.

Bell-shaped, translucent body

The box jellyfish has a body which is sometimes as big as a large bucket. It is box or bell-shaped and can weigh more than two kilograms. Up to 16 semi-transparent, extendable tentacles stream out from four projections under the bell. These tentacles in adult specimens can stretch as far as 3 metres and can contract to one quarter of their length.

Covering the tentacles are millions of stinging capsules which discharge poison through a penetrating thread into the skin of any creature which touches them. A second type of capsule produces a sticky substance which helps the tentacle stick to the victim.

Venom traps prey

The box jellyfish uses its potent venom to catch its prey. Prawns which are its main diet are immobilised and then drawn into the body cavity to be digested.

It travels at a speed around two to three knots and moves by ejecting water from its body cavity; a change in direction can be effected by altering the position of the cavity opening. If suddenly alarmed, it can turn quickly and travel at speeds up to five knots.

Excruciating pain

The sting of the box jellyfish is followed immediately by excruciating pain which increases in mounting waves. Where the skin has made contact with the tentacles, multiple brown or purple lines will appear, making the victim look as if he has been whipped. Death may occur within minutes. The greater the area of contact, the more severe the symptoms.

The box jellyfish venom contains three different ingredients. The major one causes death by shock to the heart and interferes with the breathing mechanism. Another ingredient attacks the victim's red blood cells. The skin also becomes damaged where the capsules have penetrated. If the victim survives but is not given antivenom, that part of the skin which has been stung becomes ulcerated and is often permanently scarred and discoloured.

It is highly dangerous to swim at northern beaches during the summer months when this creature is most prevalent. Swimming should be done only at patrolled beaches and only then when local people say it is safe to do so. For first aid notes on the box jellyfish, turn to Chapter 7, 'First Aid'.

The almost hypnotic tentacles of a box jellyfish trailing through mangrove roots.

B. Cropp

'The box jellyfish has a body which is sometimes as big as a large bucket.'

THE BLUE-RINGED OCTOPUS

Although it's only small, the blue-ringed octopus is one of the world's deadliest creatures. Its bite is painless and may even pass unnoticed, but its effect is immediate and sometimes fatal.

Blue-ringed octopus, *Hapalochlaena lunulata*.

Opposite top: The highly venomous blue-ringed octopus will bite when handled or disturbed. The poison can induce paralysis in about 15 minutes. Here the octopus is squirting poison into the water around a crab; the crab 'breathes' in the poisoned seawater, becomes paralysed and (bottom) then the octopus can move in and finish the job in safety.

Distribution

> ‘**When disturbed . . . the colours darken and the rings turn a brilliant electric blue colour.**’

When its tentacles are extended, the blue-ringed octopus measures only about 20 centimetres and weighs about 50 grams. It is, however, one of Australia's most venomous creatures. Its saliva contains a neuromuscular poison so potent that it causes immediate respiratory paralysis and death can occur within an hour and a half.

Found in all Australian states, there are two species of this octopus: the larger tropical species, *Hapalochlaena lunulata* and the common southern species, *H. maculosa*. The differences between the two are only minor.

The blue-ringed octopus is quite small and rarely exceeds 20 centimetres from the tip of one arm to the tip of another. Like other octopuses it has many cup-like suckers on its arms which allows it to pick up objects. Its diet is mainly crustaceans, particularly crabs and molluscs.

Poisonous saliva

The blue-ringed octopus has two large salivary or venom glands situated above its brain. A duct leads through the brain into its mouth parts which terminate in a small, parrot-like beak situated at the junction of its eight arms.

When hunting a crab, the octopus swims over it and sprays its poisonous saliva into the sea immediately surrounding it. The crab absorbs the poison and becomes paralysed within minutes allowing the octopus to seize and devour it.

Coastal rock pools

The blue-ringed octopus is usually found in rock pools around the Australian coast. When not hunting for food it sometimes shelters in rocky holes and old shells which offer protection from large predatory fish. Snapper, groper, shark and moray eels are particularly fond of octopus.

The blue-ringed octopus hunts at night. They are often washed up into small, inshore pools when the tide is rising where they may bite children or uninformed adults who may pick them up.

Identified by brilliant blue colouring

When undisturbed the blue-ringed octopus has dark brown ochre bands over its arms and body, with blue circles superimposed on these bands. When the animal is disturbed in any way or taken out of the water the colours darken and the rings turn a brilliant electric-blue colour. This dramatic and beautiful colour change and the animal's small size helps to identify it. The blue-ringed octopus should never be picked up or touched in any way, except by those trained to do so.

Paralysis within minutes

Strangely enough the bite of the blue-ringed octopus is usually painless to human beings and oftentimes goes unnoticed. However, its devastating effects are almost immediate and sometimes fatal. Extensive studies of the venom suggest that the main component is similar to the toxin found in the flesh of many poisonous fish such as toad or puffer fish. The poison interferes with the movement of impulses down the nerves of the body.

Symptoms of the bite include numbness of the mouth and tongue, blurring of vision, loss of tactile sensation, difficulty with speech and swallowing, paralysis of the legs and nausea.

If the victim is not treated, paralysis may occur within minutes, followed by unconsciousness and death can follow from heart failure due to lack of oxygen.

First aid

Full first aid notes are given in the relevant chapter, but it is worth noting here that no antivenom exists for the blue-ringed octopus. In the event of a bite from this creature, it is usually essential to carry out mouth to mouth resuscitation and cardiac massage until the effects of envenomation have subsided. This may take several hours, but quite simply means the difference between life and death for the victim. ●

Large, dark eyes and a prominent snout are two distinctive features of the blue shark. Even when badly cut or injured, the blue shark keeps on feeding and has shown a remarkable insensitivity to pain.

Photo by Ron and Valerie Taylor

SHARKS

Facts and myths create mystery

Shark! The mere word fills you with terror; few people can even think rationally about these streamlined, aristocratic predators of the seas. Millions of words have been written about them and their habits; films have been dedicated to the giant monsters but how much has our knowledge of sharks been distorted in their wake?

It is not hard to paint the typical picture of a shark: the sleek blue-grey shape, the triangular fin cutting the surface of the water and the gaping, razor-toothed jaws. But for ichthyologists, scientists who study fish, sharks are set apart from the other fish by three quite different major features. The skeleton which is made not from bone, but of a tough, flexible substance called cartilage. The raspy skin, composed of thousands of small hard scales which end in protruding points. Multiple gill slits rather than a single opening to the gills as in other fish.

Most of these features are considered to be relatively primitive, indicating a very ancient lineage. Sharks are believed to have evolved from large, armour-plated ancestors which lived in the oceans 400 million years ago. The lineages of the sharks and the modern bony fishes separated 350 million years ago, and some 100 million years ago sharks had developed the streamlined shape and powerful muscles which made them so successful as predators that they have since had little evolutionary pressure to change.

Replaceable teeth

A shark's teeth are not fixed into the bone of the jaw as in most animals, but embedded in the gums and are formed continuously. When a tooth is lost or falls out, one in the row behind it takes its place. In young, very active sharks the teeth may be replaced as often as every eight to ten days. The shape of the teeth varies according

● **Great white shark measuring 6.1 metres with a girth of 5.64 metres was killed at Twofold Bay, NSW**

to diet. Large oceanic sharks such as the mako and white shark have sharp, triangular teeth, from 8 to 19 centimetres long, for tearing at the flesh of their victims which include large fish such as tuna and marine mammals such as sea lions. Smaller sharks such as dogfish have flat plates for crushing the hard shells of the crustaceans and small invertebrates that make up their diet.

Most fish reproduce by laying thousands of eggs each time they spawn. Sharks produce eggs which hatch within the female's body. Among the few which lay eggs, the Port Jackson shark is unique. Its eggs, the largest of any fish, are enclosed in a tough case shaped into a spiral and are occasionally washed up on the shore attracting the attention of beachcombers who know them as 'mermaid's purses'. Some species give birth to live young, usually fully developed replicas of adults. As few as two and as many as eighty young are produced each year.

The sand shark has particularly aggressive young. Of 30 or so young sharks that begin life inside the female's body, two develop much more quickly than the rest. These precocious young devout cannibals devour the less advanced embryos as well as other eggs that the female continues to ovulate, remaining inside the female's body for up to a year.

Mermaid's purse (above), the colloquial name for the horny egg case of a shark.

The great white shark (below), the reef water scavenger takes another victim.

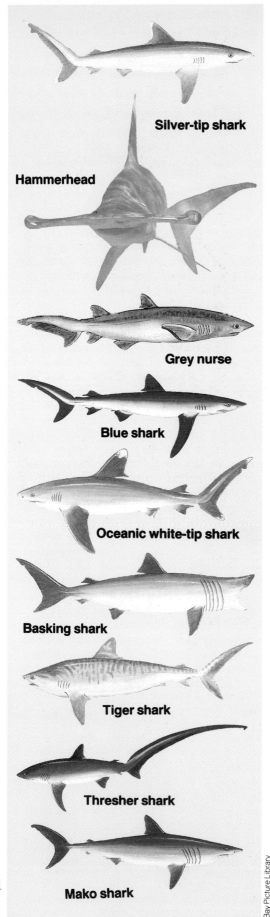

Silver-tip shark

Hammerhead

Grey nurse

Blue shark

Oceanic white-tip shark

Basking shark

Tiger shark

Thresher shark

Mako shark

Scavenger and predator
— the dangerous tiger
shark.

Shark attacks show some pattern

Compared to the appalling road carnage, shark fatalities pale into insignificance: in the past 150 years or so, there have been only about 100 reported fatal shark attacks in Australia.

The number of attacks on beaches around Sydney, Newcastle and Wollongong have dropped sharply since 1937 when systematic meshing was introduced. To protect swimming beaches a trawler sets long nets along each beach, retrieving them two or three times a week, usually with some catches.

Attempts to devise protection for the individual swimmers have not been very successful. Repellents designed during World War II were composed of copper acetate to repel sharks and a dye to camouflage the swimmer. They had little effect on sharks but seemed to boost the confidence of sailors and airmen adrift in the water.

Contrary to some popular belief, sharks do not attack swimmers indiscriminately. Some will lunge at humans almost in self-defence. Although there is ample evidence that sharks did kill and devour humans, it is unlikely that any species regularly preys on them.

The most notorious sharks involved in attacks are the White Pointer, Mako, Tiger and Whaler sharks.

Another myth which can be discarded is that sharks attack only under certain conditions. Attacks have been recorded on clear and overcast days, in clear or murky water, during the day or at night, close to the shore or in the middle of the ocean.

Still, some patterns do emerge from available statistics: most attacks took place between November and March, within 200 metres of the shore, near the surface and in warm water — Australia's main bathing conditions.

The grey nurse shark (above) probably has a reputation worse than it deserves. As yet there are no reports linking this shark to any unprovoked attacks. During the 1840s the grey nurse was heavily fished for its liver which provided oil for lamps.

The great white (below) swims with a stiff, short tail motion, unlike other sharks who glide sinuously through the water. When attacking it rolls its eyes back to show the white bony rear of the eye socket. This mechanism protects the eyes from damage.

Various species

Among the most common inshore sharks on the Australian coastline are the bottom-dwelling species such as the carpet sharks, known by the Aboriginal name 'wobbegong'; the Port Jackson shark, which was discovered by members of the First Fleet in 1788; the gummy shark; and the white tipped shark. The largest of these, the wobbegongs, *Orectolobus* species, reach three metres in length but most are considered harmless to man unless inadvertently stepped on or deliberately provoked. They feed on rockfish, crustaceans or small invertebrates such as worms which are scavenged from the sea floor.

The gummy shark, *Mustelus antarcticus*, grows to about 1.5 metres and has the dubious distinction of supporting a commercial fishery: it is commonly sold as flake, the main staple of the fish and chip industry. One bottom-dwelling shark often seen by scuba divers is the white tipped shark, *Triaenodon apicalis*, which may reach more than two metres and is a member of the more aggressive group, the whaler sharks. Sharks such as this often incur the wrath of fishermen as they will remove the bait from a hook or even wait until a fish is caught and remove both the bait and the prize.

The group known collectively as whaler sharks are believed to be responsible for more attacks on humans than any other sharks, and often enter bays, estuaries and rivers, even penetrating into fresh water. The largest of the bronze whalers, *Carcharhinus ahenea*, grow to 3.5 metres in length and the black whaler, *C. obscurus*, may reach five metres.

The tiger shark, *Galeocerdo cuvieri*, is another open ocean species which frequently enters bays or estuaries. Reaching six metres in length, it has been credited with many attacks on man and in a feeding frenzy it is savage and fearless. Its feeding habits are indiscriminate — specimens caught near shore have been found to have tin cans, coal,

dogs and even a woman's purse in their stomachs.

The white shark, *Carcharodon carchania*, and its smaller but equally aggressive relative the mako, *Isurus oxyrinchus*, are most frequently encountered close to the eastern Australian coast during the winter months. Both are rightly regarded as the most powerful and dangerous predators of the sea. The great white shark, named 'white death' by the American writer and gamefisherman, Zane Grey, has been reported to reach nine metres in length and 10 tonnes in weight.

● Virtually indestructible the whale shark lives to 70 years, most sharks live only to 25 years.

The stories are true — sharks will make a meal of a propeller.

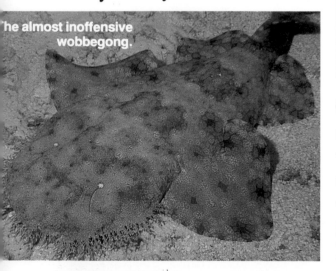

The almost inoffensive wobbegong.

● One whale shark weighing 7 tonnes was washed ashore in Anna Bay, NSW in 1964.

Tiger shark feeding. This shark became integral in the 'Shark Arm Murder' case when one tiger shark taken alive and imprisoned at a Sydney pool disgorged the tattooed arm of a murder victim.

Bad 'vibes' attract sharks

One question everybody wants answered is: what attracts sharks, what is it that triggers an attack, often a fatal one? Scientists, divers and others often produce new, at times stunning theories — and controversies.

However, certain patterns are generally accepted as characteristic of sharks.

When a fish moves in the water, it sets off a series of vibrations — usually rhythmical but weak and irregular if the fish is injured. Sharks detect these vibrations up to half a kilometre away, through a series of sensors, known as the lateral line, and follow them to the source until the prey can be located visually.

While blood in the water may not be the prime method of finding their prey, sharks do react to it. Blood, even highly diluted — certainly much less than needed to tinge the water red — can be detected by sharks; their olfactory senses are so acute that in some cases they can even spot chemicals in the water at lower concentrations than sophisticated scientific methods.

The combination of blood in the water and the irregular pulsations, such as set off by a wounded fish, often produce the so-called 'feeding frenzy' in which sharks will lunge and bite at almost anything — metal, debris or even other sharks. Make sure you're not included. . .

THE ANNA BAY MONSTER

Big male shark forced on land

A friend had called in to tell me of a huge monster washed up on Stockton Bight, near Newcastle; it was twenty-five feet long, had tusks, and altogether was something quite extraordinary.

With memories of the Tasmanian Monster in mind, I was at first a bit sceptical about it, but a report of this sort is too much for me to pass over without verifying things for myself. He had taken the trouble to come and tell me, so I thanked him and decided to go down next day and have a look.

Through the drifting spray I could make out the unmistakable figure of a lone fisherman a good mile and a half down the beach. Half a mile beyond him was a dark object and beyond that the beach just faded into misty nothingness. As I came up with the fisherman and after the usual greetings I asked about the "Monster".

"Yes, there was something along the beach," he said casually.

"It was washed up yesterday, but I haven't had a look at it yet."

Black mass

He quickly wound in his line and together we walked towards the great black mass well up on the beach. As we approached it I could see a fin and had made up my mind it was just a small hump-backed whale, when I noticed also that it had ridges running the length of the body.

Excitedly I quickened my step and in the brightening light could now make out rows of white spots all over the creature's back and sides.

"Hey! Jim," I shouted. "Do you know what this is? It's a whale shark or rhineodon, and as far as I know this is the first one to be washed up on our coastline."

The shark was lying on its side with most of the other side buried in the sand, but its head had twisted around in such a manner that the front part of the animal was really on its back. This enabled us to start at the cavernous mouth and examine the rows of minute, rasp-like teeth.

The light was not good enough for pictures so I got the steel tape out and we took some measurements. The mouth was four feet from corner to corner, and at the end of the head, not underneath, as in most sharks. If you could picture a huge catfish, you would have a good comparison.

The overall length was just on 9 metres, and the girth which could not be measured, had to be taken by measuring half of the shark. This was estimated at 5.1 metres, which was rather amazing, just 4 metres less than its entire length.

The spread of the tail was exactly 250 centimetres — 2.5 metres — and it took great effort to lift the top lobe of the tail clear of the ground.

Seven tonnes

The pectoral fin measured 1.9 metres along the outside edge, and the top lobe of the tail was 2.3 metres in from the tail joint. Using a well-known formula, I estimated the weight of the shark at seven tonnes — quite a lot of shark.

It was a male shark and had apparently been forced ashore during the heavy seas of the past week and, having got into the shallow water it was pounded about to such an extent that it probably suffocated. There were no marks of the shark being attacked by killers and it was in a very good state of preservation.

The first glimpse of one of these sharks gives an unusual sensation. You may be looking about in the water when suddenly you become aware of a number of spots moving about, then the shape of the shark is made out and the long ridges extending the length of the body lead your vision to the enormous tail slowly swinging in an arc of 5 to 6 metres.

These monsters are harmless and gentle and have never been known to attack man or boat after being harpooned. In any case, their teeth would be useless to bite anyone with and are used mainly to hinder the escape of any small fish from the cavernous mouth. Literally thousands of teeth are in numbers of rows in both the upper and lower jaws and are placed right at the tip of the mouth.

Postscript: After the local council became alarmed at the prospect of having several tonnes of rotting shark near its housing estate, a large trench was dug and the old whale shark pushed into it with a mighty thump. Samples of the teeth and hide were gathered for the Australian Museum by Athel D'Ombrain and all that remained of the first whale shark to come ashore on our coasts was a slight lump on the billiard table flat sand. The tail was left at Anna Bay as a souvenir.

Athel D'Ombrain *Fish Tales* ●

Snakes Alive!

Australian snakes are overall the most deadly in the world. Even those we consider only mildly venomous would rank highly on any world list. Here we look at ten snakes that range in venom toxicity from the almost benign eastern small-eyed snake to the highly dangerous death adder.

DEATH ADDER

The common death adder, *Acanthophis antarcticus*.

The death adder conceals itself by burrowing under leaves, leaving only a portion of its back and tail exposed. The death adder (bottom) has a small elliptical eye like a cat's eye and a blunt, coffin-shaped head.

ANT C&D Frith

The death adder strikes with amazing speed, usually close to the ground, causing bites to the foot, ankle or hand. Its venom is extremely neurotoxic, capable of causing paralysis and death; 50 per cent of its victims died in the days before the antivenom was developed.

Bay Picture Library

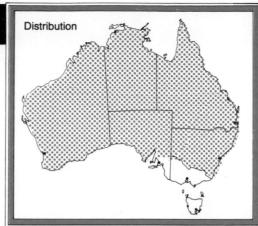

Distribution

In Australia there are 25 species of snakes considered dangerous to man. Of these, the venom of the death adder is rated as the fifth most toxic. The snake produces an average yield of 85 milligrams of venom and the maximum yield reported is an enormous 235 milligrams.

The death adder or 'deaf adder' is widely distributed throughout most of the continent although it is not found in Tasmania and experts are very doubtful that it exists in Victoria. Although there are two species in Australia, the common death adder, *Acanthophis antarcticus* and the desert death adder, *A. pyrrhus*, there are only slight differences between these two snakes.

Said to resemble the overseas viper, the death adder has many colour variations but is not difficult to identify. It has a distinctive blunt, coffin-shaped head, a thick-set body and a very thin, rat-like tail which is particularly conspicuous in well-fed specimens.

The belly is usually cream or greyish with dark brown or grey spots. Most specimens have cross bands of different colours which provide a dark-light colour pattern, helping it blend in with its environment. The snake's overall appearance may be light brown, reddish brown or even black, depending on where it is found. The snake's eye is small and elliptical like a cat's eye.

Dry habitat preferred

The death adder favours sandy, low scrub localities where it conceals itself by burrowing under leaves, sand or gravel, leaving only a portion of its back and tail exposed.

It is mainly nocturnal and is particularly active on warm nights when it is often observed crossing or lying on bush tracks. The death adder is viviparous; litters of 15 to 20 young are born each year. Most specimens grow to a length between 38 and 50 centimetres and the maximum length recorded is 1.1 metre.

Sluggish unless trodden on

Usually the death adder looks very sluggish and this may be part of its behaviour pattern; the colour patterns of its body always provide excellent camouflage whenever it lies perfectly still. Keeping its body still but wriggling its rat-like tail also helps it attract prey. Birds mistake the thin tail for a worm and pounce upon it, whereupon the snake attacks and kills the bird which it quickly devours.

The diet of a death adder also includes mice, small rats, frogs and lizards. The snake's sluggishness quickly changes to galvanised action if it is accidentally trodden on; most bite victims have been bushwalkers who have stepped on a partly submerged death adder lying across a bush track.

Rapid, accurate strike

There is strong evidence to suggest that the

ANT.

death adder only strikes when touched or trodden on; people have stood close to the snake and even stamped up and down without it attempting to strike.

However the death adder is aggressive by nature and when irritated or annoyed it flattens its entire body and strikes with amazing speed and accuracy. If discovered during the day, it makes no attempt to escape and is therefore a serious danger to people walking near its hiding place. Most other Australian snakes will retreat if they pick up a vibration of an intruder's approach.

The snake has a very efficient biting apparatus but never wastes its venom by striking an inanimate object. Its fangs are among the longest of Australian snakes; an average length of 6.2 millimetre and a maximum length of 8.3 millimetre have been recorded.

The fangs are particularly mobile and the bone that is attached to the fang is able to rotate forward. This enables the fang to enter its victim at right angles which means the venom can penetrate more deeply. Bush walkers are well ad-

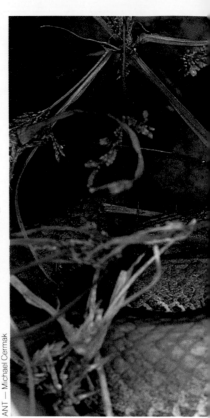

ANT — Michael Cermak

The body colour of a death adder (above) varies according to its habitat and acts as an effective camouflage.

A large male death adder (left) showing its cream underbelly, unique square-shaped head and whip-like tail.

With fangs the longest among Australian snakes and an efficient biting apparatus, the death adder (above right) secures its prey easily.

A large death adder feeding on a captured skink (right).

ANT R&D Keller

vised to wear sturdy footwear in snake country and carry a torch around the camp site after sundown.

Immediate pressure bandage

First aid treatment is important for the victim of a death adder bite. To stop the venom spreading to vital parts of the body, a broad pressure bandage should be wound around the bite site as soon as possible. Jeans or other clothing should not be taken off as the movement of the victim's body will assist the venom in entering the blood stream. Keep the bitten limb as still as possible.

The bandage should be wound tightly, as if binding a sprained ankle and should be extended well up the limb. If the leg has been bitten, a splint should be tied to the leg to help keep it immobilised. If the bite has occurred on the hand or forearm, the arm should be bandaged to the elbow and the arm placed in a sling.

Fortunately these days an antivenom exists for death adder bites and the victim should be taken to the nearest doctor or hospital as soon as possible. ●

ANT R&D Keller

COPPERHEAD

Bay Picture Library

The deadly copperhead snake, *Austrelaps superbus*, is not a snake to provoke or play games with. It is highly dangerous to humans. If provoked, it raises its forebody from the ground and flattens its neck, angry and hissing ready to strike. Its extremely potent venom is mainly neurotoxic, attacking the nerves of the body, but it also contains some blood destroying properties.

However, this snake is not aggressive by nature and is much more likely to retreat, wriggling off into the undergrowth, than to attack. If one is bitten by such a snake a broad constrictive bandage should be applied over the bitten area and the limb immobilised, then immediately medical advice sought. An effective antivenene is available.

The copperhead has a robust, thickset body with a small head that is slightly distinct from the neck. It usually has scales around its lips edged with cream, giving a distinct striped appearance. In New South Wales it is usually about one metre in length but in Victoria and Tasmania it has been known to grow as long as 1.7 metres.

Its colour is extremely variable. In New South

The copperhead, *Austrelaps superbus,* is not a snake to be taken lightly. Fortunately its copper-colouring which often appears almost iridescent makes it unmistakable (above).

The copperhead (below left) gives an indication of how the body colour of these snakes may vary. This species is almost black having little of the 'blue'. Distinctive though is the band tonings of copper along the body.

Copperheads are usually found in marshy areas, swamps and creeks and if left undisturbed will begin to form large colonies. Unfortunately they can be terrible 'neighbours' — they are prone to eat each other (bottom left).

> **'If one is bitten . . . a broad constrictive bandage should be applied and the limb immobilised.'**

Wales it is predominantly black, brown or tan on the back, while further south it may be either black, reddish brown or copper coloured. The undersurface is yellow or dark grey. The scales on the side of its body are usually enlarged and coloured yellow or white.

The copperhead is found in predominantly coastal areas, from the eastern highlands of New South Wales, through Victoria to the southeastern corner of South Australia. It is much more tolerant of the cold than other Australian snakes and has even penetrated into the southern half of Tasmania. It is also found on the Bass Strait islands. Copperheads are the last snakes to hibernate in the winter and the first to reappear in the spring. They have even been observed sunbasking in the middle of winter despite the freezing conditions.

Cluster in thick grass

This species is found in marshy areas, swamps and creeks. They cluster in thick tussocky grass, stone heaps, tree roots and in or under rotten logs. If undisturbed, they occasionally congregate in large colonies. They eat frogs, lizards and warm-blooded mammals. They are also highly prone to eating each other.

The copperhead is a hardy species and is active during both day and night, though it is not frequently encountered. It is ovoviviparous, bearing live young which are produced from soft-shelled eggs inside the mother. There may be up to 20 young in one litter. These usually measure about 17 to 20 centimetres at birth and are often marked with a dark collar on the nape of the neck and a dark vertebral line. This may or may not fade as the snake matures.

Bay Picture Library

41

Although it has a particularly toxic venom, the spotted black snake is not considered highly dangerous, since it only produces small amounts of venom.

SPOTTED BLACK SNAKE

Deadly venom but in small doses

The spotted black snake, *Pseudechis guttatus*, also known as the blue-bellied black snake, has the dubious distinction of possessing the most potent venom of its genus — even more toxic than that of the king brown snake. However, its relatively low venom yield prevents it taking on extremely dangerous proportions. According to the Commonwealth Serum Laboratories and the Queensland Museum, its low venom output places it well outside the top ten dangerous snakes.

The spotted black snake is fairly accommodating in its habitat requirements. Although it shows a strong preference for dry inland areas, it is also found in moist coastal forests and along inland river systems.

Like many other snakes, the spotted black snake has various colorations. Type specimens are glossy black, with a blue-grey ventral surface. Other specimens may have a few cream scales, while some are almost all cream, with black edges to the scales.

The head and body of this species tend to be indistinct, merging together with no change in diameter. Most mature specimens reach about 1.25 metres in length, but some grow to 2 metres.

The colour variations should not hinder its identification as it has a characteristic display when confronted. It flattens out its body to an extraordinary extent, and hisses so loudly, and for such a prolonged period, that it sounds as if it is whistling.

As with the other members of the genus, the spotted snake is by no means aggressive. When disturbed it prefers to seek cover, and will only attack if it is genuinely threatened.

Daytime hunter

Small mammals, frogs and reptiles make up the spotted snake's diet. It is basically a daytime hunter, but in periods of hot weather it may become at least partly nocturnal.

The reproduction technique of the spotted snake is subject to some conjecture. Although it has been reported to produce live young, it seems more likely that is oviparous, that is, egg-laying. It was observed in 1979, on three occasions, laying eggs, with clutches of up to 13 eggs; it is highly unlikely that it is both oviparous and ovoviparous. The eggs hatched after 11–12 weeks, with the young averaging about 28 centimetres in length.

The low venom output of this species ensures that it is less dangerous than most other venomous snakes, and its shy habits tend to keep it out of the way of most people. However, the venom is quite toxic, and a bite should be taken seriously. Severe localised pain and tenderness of the lymph nodes are the most common symptoms. The venom contains coagulants, haemolysins, neurotoxins, and cytotoxins; it is effectively treated with black snake or tiger snake antivenom.

ANT S. Wilson

RED-BELLIED BLACK SNAKE

Attractive but poisonous

The red-bellied black snake, *Pseudechis porphyriacus*, has a wide distribution, covering most of the east coast, through central western New South Wales, Victoria and into south-east South Australia. Unfortunately for this particularly beautiful snake, its habitat corresponds almost exactly with the areas of peak human population. Subsequently it finds itself persecuted more than most other snake species.

There is very little justification for the reputation this snake has. It is certainly venomous, and a bite from a large specimen could endanger the life of a child; there have been fatalities in the past attributed to this snake. But today the chances of a fatality are quite remote, especially considering how shy this species is. When disturbed it will endeavour to find shelter, and only adopts an aggressive stance as a last resort. Even then, its display is mostly bluff, and it takes a good deal of provocation to actually force it into attack.

The red-bellied black snake is perhaps the most attractive of our snakes. The body colour is a glossy black, sometimes with a touch of purple, with the side of the body a vibrant orange or red. The underside is generally dull pink, not red as might be assumed from the name.

Some specimens of this species may reach over 2.5 metres in length, but the more common length is 1–1.5 metres.

Despite heavy human predation, the red-bellied black snake is still fairly common around creeks and swamps, even in urban areas. It is a skilled and active hunter, feeding on frogs, small mammals and reptiles. It is somewhat cannibalistic, although it does not feed on its own kind to the same extent as many other species.

Useful against vermin

In urban areas this snake makes a useful pest exterminator, and does a very good job of keeping down rat and mouse populations. For this reason it deserves to be left alone and not molested. It will also feed on rabbits, and use their burrows for shelter. Where these are not available, it will rest in hollow logs, under rocks, or among loose rubbish and vegetation. It is a good swimmer and often enters the water to hunt fish and eels.

Young red-bellied black snakes are born live, and measure about 20 centimetres at birth. Brood sizes vary, numbering from 8 to 40, with 10–15 being most common.

The venom of the red-bellied black snake is one of the least toxic of our dangerous snakes. The symptoms are generally localised, and include severe pain, haemorrhaging, and localised paralysis. Medical treatment is important, despite the relative low toxicity of this snake, and first aid should follow the guidelines laid down in the relevant chapter. Since this snake is so loathe to strike, there should be no excuse for being bitten by it, unless it is accidentally trodden on. Most bites occur when it is constantly interfered with.

The red-bellied black snake is probably the most attractive of all Australian snakes, and has a reputation quite out of keeping with its limited powers to inflict harm.

ANT J. Weigel

COLLETT'S SNAKE

Flattens before striking

Collett's snake is found only in sparsely populated central Queensland, and for this reason little is known of its habits. Most authorities agree, however, that this is definitely a species to avoid.

The colour of Collett's snake, *Pseudechis colletti*, varies somewhat, largely because its body scales are individually coloured in pinks, browns and creams, in a rather haphazard pattern. The belly is pale orange to yellow. The overall effect is quite striking, and certainly very attractive.

Adult specimens normally attain a length of 1.25 metres, with 1.8–2 metres being exceptional but not unknown in this species.

Collett's snake is a diurnal hunter, preying on small mammals and birds, reptiles and amphibians.

Some controversy continues over this snake's mode of reproduction. Worrell recorded that it is live-bearing, with 12 or more young in a litter. Gow, however, noted that it is an egg-layer, with up to 13 eggs in a clutch and the hatchlings measuring 37 centimetres.

Research needed

As Gow's work is more recent, and he, like Worrell, is an experienced herpetologist, his view is to be preferred. The discrepancy highlights the need for more research into some of our more remote species — this was shown by the recent work on the fierce snake. For many years virtually unknown, almost overnight it became infamous as the world's most venomous land snake.

Collett's snake is, on the rare occasions when it is encountered, quite unaggressive. With provocation, however, it flattens out its body and prepares to strike. If treated with respect it presents no danger.

The venom of this species appears to be similar to that of the mulga or king brown snake, *P. australis*, a close relative of Collett's snake. In toxicity it should therefore not be underestimated, although it is less dangerous than most other venomous species.

The full extent of its potential to cause serious illness has not yet been ascertained, and depends largely on just how much venom it produces. Until such research has been undertaken, it should be regarded as dangerous, and given a wide berth.

Collett's snake inhabits the black soil plains of central western Queensland.

ANT S. Wilson

47

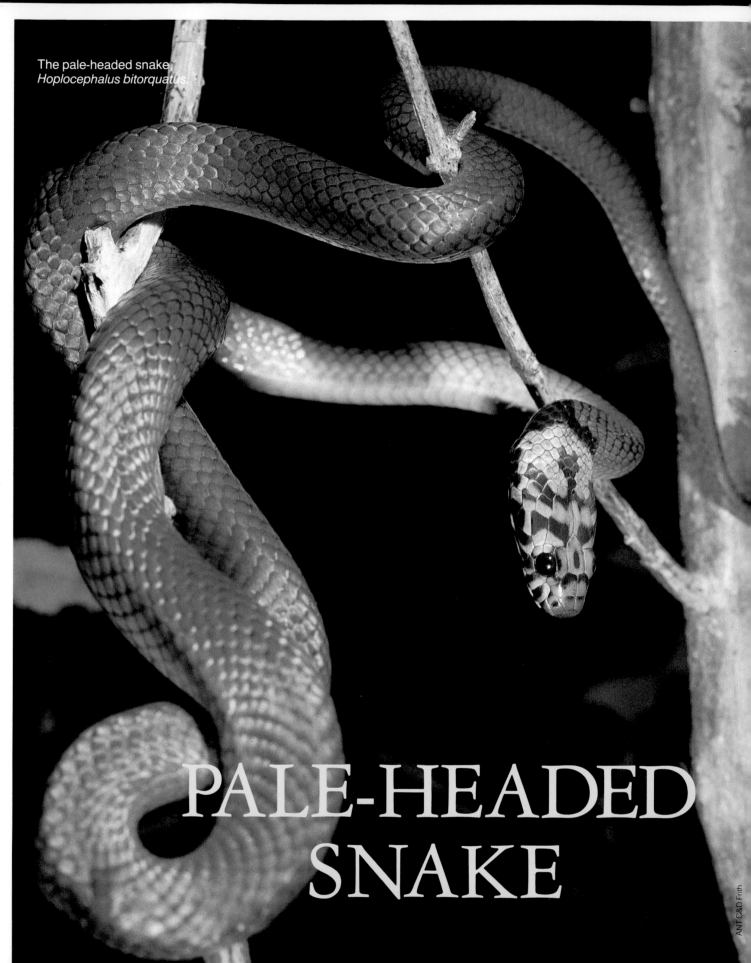

The pale-headed snake, *Hoplocephalus bitorquatus*.

PALE-HEADED
SNAKE

This quick, agile snake is aggressive by nature and should never be provoked. Although its venom is not lethal, it is quite potent and can cause considerable pain, local swelling and fever. A bite from a large pale-headed snake should be treated immediately.

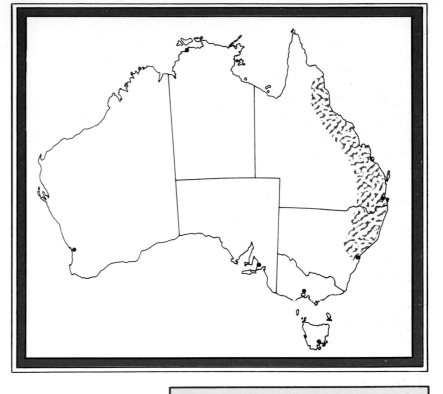

The pale-headed snake, *Hoplocephalus bitorquatus*, belongs to the genus which contains the few species of Australian elapid snakes that are tree-climbers but only one species of this genus is consistently so, the pale-headed snake being only partly arboreal.

The pale-headed snake is found in inland eastern Australia from about Gosford in New South Wales through Queensland, where it is most common, to Cape York Peninsula. It lives in wooded areas, rainforests and temperate woodlands. It is a nocturnal species and shelters under the loose bark of trees or inside hollows in branches.

Large white flapping ears

The pale-headed snake has a broad head, which is quite distinct from the neck. As its name suggests, the head is coloured a distinctive pale grey with black blotches or spots on it. The lips and often also the chin of the snake are barred with black. On the sides of the head near the neck it sometimes has white or yellow spots which, when the snake is angry or afraid and its neck is puffed out, resemble two large, white, flapping ears.

Although the Latin name of the snake suggests that it has two collars, it actually has no collars. However it has two patches at the nape of its neck, one coloured white and the other brown or grey.

The back of its body is light to dark grey or light greyish-brown and the underside is creamy grey, often with darker flecks or freckles. This snake grows usually to about half a metre in size although specimens reaching over a metre in length have been recorded. The body is moderately robust.

As with all species belonging to the genus *Hoplocephalus*, it has a ridge or keel at the end of each ventral scale to aid it in climbing trees. The scales on its back however, are smooth.

The pale-headed snake has been known in captivity to eat small mammals such as mice but in its natural habitat it lives entirely on small lizards such as geckoes and skinks.

It bears live young but it is not known exactly how many are produced at one time. ●

The pale-headed snake is especially aggressive when aroused. A bite from a large specimen should be treated promptly.

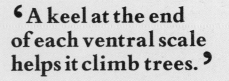

'A keel at the end of each ventral scale helps it climb trees.'

The attractively marked Stephen's banded snake is most commonly found in wet sclerophyll forests along the east coast of northern New South Wales and southern Queensland.

STEPHEN'S BANDED SNAKE

Loves climbing trees

Stephen's banded snake, *Hoplocephalus stephensi*, is hardly a commonly encountered snake; its nocturnal and arboreal nature puts it outside the normal human scope. When confronted, however, it will not hesitate to defend itself. Like the other members of its genus, the pale-headed snake and the broad-headed snake, it is an aggressive species that only requires mild provocation.

One of our more attractive snake species, Stephen's banded snake ranges through north-eastern New South Wales to south-eastern Queensland. Occasionally specimens are found as far south as Gosford, but for the most part they favour a warmer climate.

Wet sclerophyll forest and rainforest are preferred by this snake. It is an adroit climber, and spends a great deal of its time in trees, either resting in a hollow limb or hunting through the branches.

As the name suggests, type specimens of Stephen's banded snake are distinguished by broad, black bands along the length of the body. Some specimens may be unbanded, and can only be positively identified by a scale count. There are 21 rows at the mid-body, with a single anal plate. Ventral scales number 220–250, while sub-caudals number 50–70.

Not too dangerous

The principle coloration away from the bands is a soft, creamy brown, and the underside is cream with black patches. The head is predominantly black, with splashes of cream.

Stephen's banded snake is not considered highly dangerous to man, but a bite could probably cause a serious illness in children or elderly casualties if not treated promptly. The venom is largely neurotoxic, and contains a strong thrombin; it is effectively neutralised by tiger snake antivenom.

When provoked, even slightly, Stephen's banded snake launches into a threatening display. It rises into a striking position, with the neck looped and the head held high. If this threat fails to dissuade an aggressor, it will strike, often repeatedly.

Lizards, birds and small mammals are consumed by this species, which hunts at night, generally through the upper limbs of trees. Young are born live, and measure about 15–20 centimetres; adults are generally about 60 centimetres long, but grow as large as 1 metre. ●

The broad-headed snake bears a striking resemblance to the diamond python; it is declining in numbers due to excessive collection and the spreading suburban sprawl.

BROAD-HEADED SNAKE

Facing slow extinction

The broad-headed snake is a particularly dangerous species, not only because of its fairly potent venom, but also because of its striking resemblance to the harmless diamond python. At least one death has occurred when it was mistakenly picked up as a non-venomous snake. Only through close examination is it possible to tell the two species apart — and for all but the experienced, handling of the broad-headed snake is not advised.

The broad-headed snake is found only within a radius of about 250 kilometres of Sydney. It prefers rocky areas, particularly areas dominated by Hawkesbury sandstone and eucalypt associations. The large human population in this area, and the growing number of amateur herpetologists, are responsible for this snake's slow decline in numbers.

It was once fairly common, but development and excessive collection have reduced its numbers considerably. Irregular bands of yellow scales, on a dark brown to black background, make the broad-headed snake a distinctive species quite difficult to miss. Towards the front of the head, and around the lips, the bands become more concentrated, and form a solid yellow area. It is not a large snake, most reaching only 75 centimetres; the largest specimen recorded so far was just over 1.5 metres.

Handle with care

A mid-body scale count will quickly separate this snake from the diamond python. The latter has 40 or more scale rows, whereas the broad-headed snake has 21. However, it is a species that does not take at all well to handling, and even experienced herpetologists have some difficulty with it.

The broad-headed snake feeds chiefly on small lizards, but if the opportunity presents itself, it will also feed on frogs and small mammals. Young broad-headed snakes are born live, being produced in litters of 8–20.

When provoked, the broad-headed snake immediately assumes an aggressive stance. It rises up, holding its neck in an 'S' shape. If it is not left alone, it will strike out repeatedly.

The venom of the broad-headed snake has not been studied closely, but if it is similar to the other snakes of its genus, its potency is not excessively high. Nor does it seem to yield a large amount of venom. This is not to say, of course, that a bite from this snake is not painful. It is, and the casualty can expect severe headaches, vomiting, partial loss of vision, sweating and general muscular fatigue. The venom is basically neurotoxic, and without treatment the casualty will suffer greatly. Tiger snake antivenom is effectively used in treatment.

Auscape Int. J C Wombey

The rough-scaled snake is a species that does not appreciate the least amount of provocation.

ROUGH-SCALED SNAKE

Bites first, asks questions later

Everyone knows about gunmen with itchy trigger fingers. Well, this is a snake with itchy 'fang fingers'. The rough-scaled snake will not hesitate to put its potent venom to work, if provoked, and is certainly a species to avoid.

The rough-scaled snake, *Tropidechis carinatus*, occurs in two apparently isolated populations, one around the Clarence River, in New South Wales, extending into south-eastern Queensland, and the other on the east coast of Queensland between Nambour and Tully.

Identifying the rough-scaled snake can be a difficult task, and one that requires close examination. The only way it can be distinguished from the keel back snake, which also occurs in this area, is by counting the body scales. The keel back has 15–17 rows of mid-body scales, and a divided anal plate, while the rough-scaled snake has 23 rows and single anal plate.

It is a pity these two snakes are so similar, for the keel back is often persecuted as a dangerous species when, in fact, it is harmless. It rarely bites, and is one of the few native animals able to eat the cane toad without suffering ill effects. If only for this reason it should be encouraged, rather than shunned.

The rough-scaled snake has a large distinct head and olive-green to brown body colour; the undersurface is paler, with occasional light green patches. Dark cross bands are found in most specimens.

Not a fussy eater

Rainforests and well watered areas are favoured haunts of the rough-scaled snake. It is mainly active during the day, except in warm weather when it may become partly nocturnal. Like most snakes, it is none too fussy about what it eats. Small mammals, reptiles and amphibians, particularly frogs, are all devoured with relish.

The rough-scaled snake is known to have caused several deaths and is believed responsible for others in which the offending snake was not positively identified. A bite from this species should be treated with the utmost urgency. The venom is neurotoxic and causes considerable muscle damage and disturbances in blood clotting.

Even experienced snake handlers are wary of the rough-scaled snake. It does not settle down to life in captivity and remains nervous and aggressive at all times. In the wild it is normally quite shy and will retire if given the chance. But with mild provocation it adopts an aggressive stance and will make repeated strikes until it is left alone.

Tiger snake antivenom is effectively used as treatment for rough-scaled snake bites, and with prompt attention there is little chance of death. Nevertheless, it is a species that deserves a wide berth if seen in the wild. ●

ANT Frithoto

The eastern small-eyed snake is a nocturnal species, thought for many years to be of little danger to man.

EASTERN SMALL-EYED SNAKE

Prefers night life

For many years the eastern-small eyed snake was considered a venomous species of little danger to man. Recent research has shown this belief to be quite mistaken; at least one person has died from a bite inflicted by this species, and its venom has been shown to be quite potent.

The eastern small-eyed snake, *Cryptophis nigrescens*, occurs along the entire length of the east coast, reaching inland as far as the Great Dividing Range. Within this area it is found in a variety of habitats, from heaths to rainforests, with a decided preference for rocky, sandstone areas.

The dorsal colour of this species is glossy black or grey. The belly is variable, and may be white, cream or pink and, in some specimens, with dark blotches.

The young are born live, in litters of 2–5, and measure about 11 centimetres at birth. Adults reach a maximum of 1.2 metres.

The eastern small-eyed snake is a nocturnal species that feeds predominantly on frogs and lizards. During the day it retreats to hollow logs, rock crevices and fallen leaf litter.

Painful bite

Research into the venom of this species has produced figures that do not entirely correspond with its effects. The Commonwealth Serum Laboratories and the Queensland Museum both place this species about number fifteen in their lists of dangerous snakes.

Despite this, researchers recognise that it is a dangerous species. A bite from the eastern small-eyed snake can be very painful, and result in severe headaches and muscle damage.

The one recorded fatality reliably attributed to this species was a 20-year-old man who died in Cairns Base Hospital in 1965. Kidney failure was the principal cause of death, brought about by muscle damage.

The eastern small-eyed snake is a good example of the need for continuing research not only on our known dangerous species, but also those regarded as harmless. In time it is quite possible that other species will be added to the list of dangerous Australians.

A prime candidate would seem to be the northern small-eyed snake, *C. pallidiceps*, a close relative of the eastern small-eyed snake. So far little research has been undertaken on this species, but in most respects it appears to be similar to its eastern relative.

ANT J. Weigel

FROM VENOMS TO ANTIVENOMS

Even the most poisonous snakes can be rendered harmless

Australian snakes have the rather dubious distinction of possessing the most dangerous venoms in the world, and in many cases an outrageously high venom output, too. The venom of our most dangerous species is far more potent than is necessary for the snake to overcome and kill its prey — the taipan carries enough venom to kill 12 000 guinea pigs — but why this is so has never been satisfactorily explained.

Snake venom is a highly developed form of saliva, injected by the snake into its victim through hollow, modified teeth known as fangs. The venom consists of a number of complex proteins which act on the prey in various ways.

Five major components are recognised: neurotoxins act on the nervous system, particularly at neuro-muscular junctions, and hinder the operation of the voluntary muscles; haemolysins destroy the red blood cells; thrombus, or coagulant, clots blood within its vessels; cytotoxins attack blood cells, and any other cells they contact; anti-coagulants prevent the normal clotting of the blood, resulting in bleeding.

In Australian snakes, the neurotoxins predominate, often coupled with one or more of the other venom components. There are also variations within the venom groups. The tiger snake, for example, produces venom with three distinct neurotoxins, each one independently capable of causing a degree of paralysis.

As well as these components, snake venom also contains enzymes which aid the spread of the venom through tissue. These enzymes are often referred to as 'spreading factors'.

Relative danger

When assessing the relative danger of Australia's snakes, a number of factors must be considered. It is not simply a matter of deciding which is the most potent venom. Other factors that must be borne in mind are the amount of venom the snake is able to deliver in one strike, the number of strikes it can make, the age, weight and health of the victim, and the availability of first aid and antivenom.

The interplay of these various factors makes it virtually impossible to draw up a list of snakes in order of danger. For example, the red-bellied black snake is unlikely to inflict a life-threatening bite — if the victim is in good health, not too young or old. A very young snake is unlikely to have a high enough venom output to inflict much harm. But in a sick, elderly or very young victim, the result of a bite could be life-threatening.

The only rating system currently available that seems to have any real use to victims of snake bite is the Commonwealth Serum Laboratories' LD_{50} test. This accurately gauges the effects of snake venom on mice, and gives a toxicity rating. Its drawback is that it does not fully take into account the average venom yield from each snake.

Top five ranking

Using the LD_{50} test, it is possible to place the Australian snakes in order of toxicity. The top five potential killers are, in order of venom potency, fierce snake, taipan, tiger snake, death

adder and king brown snake.

It should be remembered that the LD_{50} uses mice, not humans. The effects of snake venom on men and mice varies, and one is not necessarily a good indicator of the other.

Having established what a venom is, and, according to the LD_{50} test, which snakes are the most dangerous, the obvious question is how do we effectively combat these venoms? The equally obvious answer is — with an antivenom.

Antivenoms have been in use for thousands of years, but in their early forms they were crude and even bizarre. Some peoples believed that if snake's bowels were eaten or applied to the wound the venom would be neutralised. The Hindus took this further, and claimed that if the victim bit off the head of the offending snake he or she would be cured.

Buried in dung

European cures were a little less bizarre, but no more effective. Goat and pig products were often applied to the wound or eaten, or if drastic action was deemed necessary, the victim was buried to the neck in dung — a spoonful of sugar would have done very little to sweeten that 'cure'.

As man penetrated once unknown lands, contacts with snakes increased, and entrepreneurs were always ready to market their own special brand of snake bite cure. Most were simple herbal mixtures that did little to counteract the effects of the poisoning but probably did wonders for the victim's confidence.

One cure that would have done anything but inspire confidence had its origins with Marco Polo — gunpowder. The wound was covered with gunpowder and set alight. The resulting explosion was supposed to cleanse the limb of all venom. Chances are it did just that — and took the injured limb with it.

Venom drips from the fangs of a deadly olive-brown sea snake (left). A researcher at Macquarie University (above) holds one of the funnel-webs kept for milking.

'Dr Struan Sutherland's work has placed Australia in the forefront of antivenom research.'

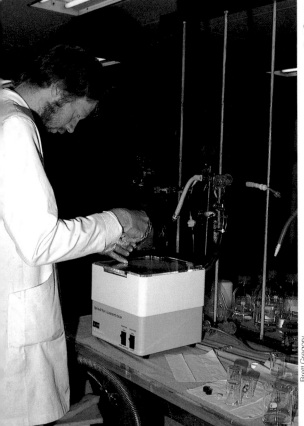

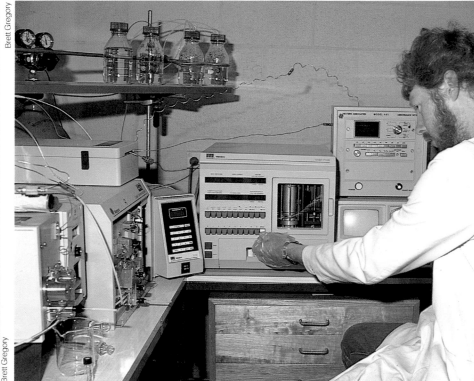

Ben Cropp

A tiger snake gives its all for science (above left). Ben Cropp, aided by his wife Lynn, tests the effectiveness of metho and vinegar against box jellyfish stings (above); see Ben's foreword for details of the experiment. At Macquarie University (left and far left) researchers led by Dr Merlin Howden conduct tests on the venom of the Sydney funnel-web. Dr Howden's team was responsible for the development of the first funnel-web antivenom.

Booze treatment

The favoured 'cure' for snake bite in Australia was alcohol. It was used so liberally that is was almost worthwhile being bitten by a snake, just to consume as much free booze as one could hold. Once again, the remedy would have done little apart from relaxing the victim; this is an important phase of first aid today, but the administering of alcohol is not recommended, as it only complicates treatment.

The first genuine breakthrough in the treatment of snake bite came in 1887 when an American, H. Sewall, discovered that by gradually injecting animals with small quantities of venom, they would build up a resistance to it, finally reaching a point where they could comfortably survive normally lethal doses.

Sewall's work was extended at the Pasteur Institute in Paris where researchers found that they could immunise other animals with the blood of an immune animal.

Early attempts at producing antivenoms were successful, but limited. The antivenoms were very specific, and only worked for single snake species. Such antivenoms are known as monovalent.

Australian research

Australian research into antivenoms began in the 1920s. Led by Dr C. H. Kellaway, the Commonwealth Serum Laboratories (CSL) developed a monovalent antivenom for the tiger snake. Work continued, and gradually antivenoms became available for most of the deadly Australian snakes. However, all the antivenoms were specific, and correct administration required the identification of the snake responsible for the bite. It was not until 1962 that a polyvalent antivenom became available, ensuring almost complete protection for Australians bitten by snakes.

Antivenoms are produced in Australia at the CSL's Victorian laboratory in Melbourne. Snake, spider and tick venoms from collectors all around Australia are sent to the laboratories where they are injected into Percheron horses. There are 250 horses on the CSL farm, all living in the lap of luxury. They undergo no stress during the inoculation and extraction processes. Inoculation is quite harmless, and extraction is as simple as donating blood for a human.

The horses are given increasing doses of venom over a period of time until they have built up sufficient antibodies to the venom. These antibodies are then extracted from the blood, purified and reduced to a useable form.

The antivenoms taken from the horses are used to treat humans suffering from snake, spider or tick poisoning. Injected into the human bloodstream, the antibodies attack the venom cells, neutralising their effects. The dose of antivenom given to a patient varies according to species responsible for the bite and, when it can be ascertained, the amount of venom injected. The age and weight of the victim makes no difference.

Side-effects

Damaging side-effects to antivenoms sometimes occur, but as techniques improve the effects are decreasing. Known as anaphylactic reactions, they were at one time a serious problem, but today it is rare for anyone to suffer severe reactions.

Most anaphylactic reactions seem to occur in patients who at some stage may have come into contact with equine protein, a constituent of the antivenoms. Polyvalent antivenoms are also more likely to bring about a reaction, since the dosage is higher than for monovalent antivenoms.

In all cases, however, it is important to remember that the cure is a good deal better than letting the venom take its course. It is never too late to administer antivenom, and as soon as appropriate precautions have been taken by the attending doctor, the antivenom should be given at the recommended dosage. ●

Spiders, Insects — and a Lonely Toad

In contrast to our plentiful supply of dangerous snakes, Australia has only three, possibly four spiders of any real danger. There are, however, a host of insects and arachnids to make up for this shortage. At the end of this chapter is the misfit of Dangerous Australians — *the lonely cane toad.*

RED-BACK SPIDER

A pint-sized killer

Contrary to popular opinion, red-backs have not decreased in numbers since the demise of the outdoor toilet. And, to set straight another misconception, it is only the female red-back that is of danger to man — but she makes up for the male's passive role by inflicting a painful bite on hundreds of people each year.

There is only one species of red-back spider, *Lactrodectus mactans hasselti*, a comb-footed spider of the family Theridiidae, which is found throughout Australia in dry habitats ranging from open forest to desert. It is closely related to the katipo of New Zealand and the black widow in north America; the latter had star billing as the death-dealing accomplice of a wicked woman in a weekly television series of the same name in the 1950s.

The male red-back is only 5 millimetres long, light brown with paler, whitish and orange markings on the upper surface of the abdomen and a red spot underneath. Though equipped with venom glands the fangs of the male are unable to effectively penetrate human skin.

The female red-back, with her distinctive red markings, is much larger than the male. Both have short fangs resembling small hairs, but only the female is dangerous to humans.

Brightly marked females

The female which is a threat to humans, reaches a length of 15 millimetres, the smoothly rounded abdomen being about the size of a pea and shiny black or dark brown in colour. The upper surface usually has a red or orange-red stripe, often with a separate dot in front of it, and the underside bears a red brand in the shape of an hourglass. The adult colour pattern is attained only with the final moult and juveniles vary markedly.

Red-backs mature in summer, at which time the females produce 3–8 egg cocoons. These are attached to the web, or concealed in the nearby retreat.

Females die after laying their eggs. The spiderlings hatch towards the end of summer, and disperse in autumn. When they have found a suitable location, they make their own webs.

In its sheltered retreat, under rocks or in soil banks, stumps or logs, the spider constructs a network of silken threads stretching outward, from which vertical threads armed with viscid globules are extended to the ground. When prey stumbles into these sticky tensioned trap lines, the lines break, springing upward and hoisting the prey into the incredibly strong web. The spider uses a comb of barbed spines on the last segment of the fourth leg to throw swathes of silk around the prey, completing the immobilisation with a bite.

Red-backs are normally only active around dusk and at night. During the day they remain concealed near their web, or hang upside down in the web itself.

Mighty hunters

Red-backs feed on prey as large as skinks and young house mice, but more often make do with passing beetles and other spiders including funnel-webs and the related trapdoor spiders.

Bites from red-back spiders are no less frequent now than when outdoor toilets were common. Every year hundreds of people are bitten by this spider. The symptoms of a bite (most bites are confined to the upper and lower limbs) are pain and localised swelling, followed by nausea, headache, cramp and, in severe cases, paralysis and death. About twelve human deaths in Australia have been attributed to bites from red-backs, but there have been none since an effective antivenene was developed by the Commonwealth Serum Laboratories in 1956. This antivenom is apparently effective if taken up to 80 hours after the venom was injected.

As the effects of a red-back bite take some time to fully reveal themselves, there is no need to panic; it may take days before treatment becomes urgent. Obviously, however, it is best to seek treatment immediately.

The female red-back spider, *Lactrodectus Mactans*.

Despite apparently having the upper hand, this red-back ultimately lost its battle with the scorpion (opposite). Adult female red-backs (left) are easily distinguished from day-old juveniles (below left).

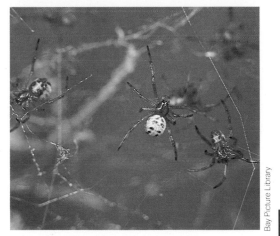

Warning colour

The distinctive red back of this spider serves as a useful warning, making it difficult to miss it if a little care is taken when moving rubbish, or placing your hands in forgotten places.

Although not related to the red-back spider, the common window or black house spider, *Ixeuticus I. robustus*, is somewhat similar in appearance. It is highly venomous and should be treated with caution. It has a shiny black abdomen and legs and grows to 1.6 centimetres. It builds its tangled web in the corners of windows or door frames, or under eaves, where it catches flies and other insect pests.

'Red-backs feed on prey as large as skinks and young house mice.'

FIDDLEBACK SPIDER

Has a preference for Adelaide suburbs . . .

Bay Picture Library.

Don't be misled by its amusing name: the fiddleback spider does have a highly venomous bite. Lesions usually appear around the bite; in extreme cases, gangrene develops.

Large areas of skin slough away to expose ulcers which take five to six weeks to heal. Severe reactions including toxic effects to various body organs may follow, especially to the kidneys, sometimes even resulting in death.

The fiddleback spider — also known as the violin spider or brown recluse — belongs to the family Scytodidae. It is thought to have originated in the Mediterranean region but is now widely spread in temperate and tropical zones of the world, especially Central and South America.

It has caused several deaths in Europe and South America. In 1974 one species of this spider, *Loxosceles refuscens*, was found in a suburb of Adelaide. It has now also been found in various country areas of South Australia. The South American species, *Loxosceles laeta* has been found in the central area of Sydney. This species, *L. laeta*, is especially dangerous causing lesions of the viscera often resulting in death.

Could be widespread

It is not known exactly how this spider came to be introduced into Australia but it is now well established, especially in the Brooklyn Park area of Adelaide. Interestingly enough, this species has actually been present in museum collections for more than 40 years but its presence 'at large'

Mainly a resident of Latin America, the fiddleback spider also occurs in some parts of South Australia. This is a young fiddleback going through its green phase.

Fiddleback spider,
Loxosceles refuscens.

has only been confirmed in recent years. Experts believe that it could be breeding in other parts of Australia.

Frequently it lives close to humans and their buildings. It is found in storerooms, sheds and occasionally even inside houses. In the wild it lurks under the bark of dead trees or under stones on the ground, usually in dry places.

The fiddleback spider grows to about the size of a redback. It looks something like a cross between a huntsman spider and a wolf spider. It has a small body and long, spindly, sprawling legs, the second pair being longer than the fourth. Both the body and the legs are covered with minute hairs.

Distinctive mark

Fiddlebacks vary in colour from light yellowish brown to dark brown and have a distinctive fiddle or violin-shaped marking on the back of the head and thorax. They have an almost pale, transparent look about them.

Unlike most spiders, this species has six eyes, all of which are a pearly white colour. It belongs to that portion of the six-eyed series of spiders which have a single passage through which air is conveyed. The fiddleback has very simple external reproductive organs. The head and thorax area is low and depressed.

The fiddleback is shy and retiring and not at all aggressive by nature. It is mainly active at night and does not congregate in colonies. It moves about only on the ground.

It spins large, irregular webs beneath stones or logs and also spins silken sacs and gets inside them, perhaps as a way of retreat from the winter cold. The silk of these sacs is hackled. It lays its eggs in a disc-shaped egg-sac which has a diameter longer than the spider's body. This sac is attached to the spider's web.

‘Frequently it lives close to humans and their buildings. It is found in storerooms, sheds and occasionally even inside houses. In the wild it lurks under the bark of dead trees or under stones.’

The female scrub tick fully bloated.

The Australian scrub tick, also known as the paralysis tick or dog tick, is a minute parasite that delivers a paralysing toxin and if not removed can eventually cause death, even in human hosts.

Ticks are notorious for the many serious diseases and ailments they can transmit or cause, but of the 59 species occurring in Australia, the scrub tick, *Ixodes holocyclus*, is one of the worst offenders. These tiny parasites are not insects but arachnids, members of the spider group.

They are found in eastern Australia between the mountains and the coast from lower Cape York Peninsula down into far eastern Victoria. They are most prevalent within 16 kilometres of the coast but they have been found further inland and are particularly abundant in rainforests. Birds carrying nymphs of this species have even been recorded in the Canberra area, but whether the tick has become established there has not yet been determined.

No preferred victim

Unlike many other ticks which feed only on the blood of certain animals, the scrub tick is not particular and any warmblooded animal will do. The most common host is the bandicoot but

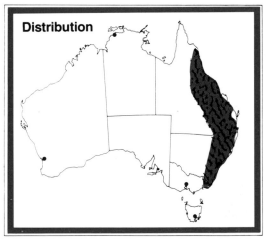

Distribution

THE AUSTRALIAN SCRUB TICK

The paralysis tick

A full engorged
Tasmanian paralysis tick.

1. This double-tailed delicate skink is badly infested with ticks all along its body. 2. The tick-infested neck of the amethystine python. 3. Ticks have picked the ears of this green-tailed possum to secure themselves. 4. Rufous rat-kangaroo with severe blight of ticks around the eyes. 5. Most frightening of all is the tick piercing human skin.

1

2

3

4

5

most small and large marsupials, including kangaroos carry scrub ticks, as do spiny ant-eaters. Many birds are affected, including chickens, ducks, parrots, crows, magpies, cur-lews and butcherbirds; pets, especially dogs; stock such as horses, cattle, sheep, goats and pigs; mice and rats. There have even been reports of zoo animals, particularly monkeys, carrying scrub ticks. Humans who visit tick-infested areas or come into contact with infested animals are also liable to be chosen as hosts.

Ticks may be found anywhere on a host's body, but tend to prefer softer skin in areas such as the groin and external genitals, the corners of the mouth and eyes, the ears and the head gener-ally. On humans they tend to hide in folds of the skin or above the hairline and have been known to attach themselves to the eardrum. On birds they keep mainly to the head and to bare or sparsely-feathered areas.

Wrong diagnosis results in death

Scrub tick paralysis is caused by a poison in the saliva which causes a progressive muscular paral-ysis in the host that may evenually affect respir-ation and heart function, resulting in death. Ac-tually, once a tick is removed the host begins to recover and in severe cases an antitoxin is avail-able. However, in certain cases where the doctor has not known that the patient was in tick country the symptoms of approaching tick paral-ysis have been confused with some other disease such as infantile paralysis. There have even been cases reported in which a bandage has been left covering the unrecognised tick until the victim died.

Ticks should never be squeezed as more poison may be thus injected into the host's body. They should be carefully plucked out using either tweezers or the 'v' of slightly open scissors.

Two related species *I. cornuatus* and *I. hirsti* are associated with similar paralysis, but further study is required before their significance can be assessed.

Responsible for many ailments

Scrub ticks are associated with various other ailments and diseases. Allergic reactions such as itching, rashes, swelling of lymph nodes and res-piratory distress have been noted and are in some cases severe.

This species is one of several responsible for the transmission of Q fever, a disease exhibiting pneumonia-like symptoms and caused by the microoganism *Coxiella burneti* which the ticks can carry. Most noted in humans, natural occur-rences of Q fever have been detected in dogs, cattle, sheep, kangaroos and bandicoots. Although the disease is usually transmitted by a tick's bite, infections in humans are thought to occur mainly through contact with the ex-cretions and secretions of infected animals.

Scrub ticks are also thought to be associated with the spread of Queensland 'tick typhus', a human disease occurring in coastal Queensland.

Complex life cycle

Ticks have a complex life cycle consisting of three parasitic stages. Immature forms are no larger than the head of a pin and are oval in shape. Thousands of these tiny creatures climb grass blades to await a passing host.

As soon as a tick touches the skin of a host, its sharp mouthparts pierce the skin and the tick be-gins to rapidly engorge itself with blood, becom-ing partially buried in the skin. In only four days a female tick can expand to as much as 400 times her original size, looking something like a blood blister, her shape now only slightly oval. Size in-creases in males are not nearly so dramatic.

The tick then drops off to digest its meal, moults and repeats the process. The female feeds during all three stages — larva, nymph, adult — the male feeds from a host only during the first two stages. Females always feed until fully engorged and paralysis is usually associated with the adult female during her final meal. While she consumes her last draught, a male aboard the same host finds her and mates with her. The male has even been observed to refresh itself with a drink from the female body during mating, by piercing her body with its mouthparts.

Fully engorged and fertilised, the adult female drops from the host, lays thousands of eggs in a single batch, then dies. On hatching some seven to nine weeks later, the tiny larvae seek hosts and renew the cycle. ●

LEECHES

The bane of the bushwalker

Bushwalkers traversing rainforests are likely to encounter the leech. Its bite is often not felt and the first indication is usually profuse bleeding from a wound.

A.N.T. Kathie Atkinson

ANT Kathie Atkinson

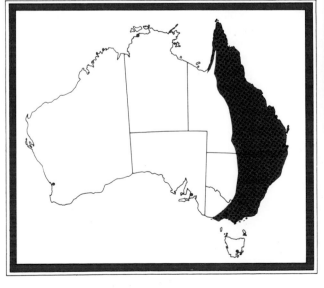

ANT R&D Keller

A fully engorged leech (above left) is well adapted to life in the wild; it can store up to five times its own bodyweight in blood.

Closely related to the earthworm, the leech (above) inhabits forests where it feeds on worms, snails and insect larvae.

Leeches have always had a bad name but their most infamous moment that no filmgoer will ever forget was their appearance in _The African Queen_. In trying to escape, Humphrey Bogart pushed his boat, _The African Queen_, and precious cargo, Katherine Hepburn, through the reed-filled estuary only to be rewarded by leeches. His back and chest were covered. The scene was an unforgetable lesson in where not to swim.

In the eastern highlands of Papua New Guinea, parasitic leeches have been found under the dorsal skin of frogs.

The leech is attracted by the warm blood of its victim. On detecting a meal in its vicinity the leech rapidly climbs to the first patch of bare skin, sinks its proboscis into the flesh and injects a chemical which prevents the blood from clotting. Thus even after it has already engorged itself the victim continues to bleed profusely from the wound.

The leech belongs to the family Hirudinea, and is closely related to the earthworm. Some years ago the most well known leech was, of course, the medicinal leech, _Hirudo medicinalis_, used for the purpose of blood-letting. The medical effectiveness of such a practice is indeed open to question, but some doctors maintain even today, that such a procedure would at least have been temporarily effective in relieving high blood pressure.

In Australia the equivalent is the freshwater leech, _Limnobdella australis_, which was apparently kept as stock in most chemist shops around the turn of the century. This leech is the most common of New South Wales leeches and is also found in Victoria and Queensland. It has large, very strong teeth.

The leech may have sharp teeth but its bite is so gentle that the insertion of the proboscis is usually not even felt. Normally the first indication of the presence of a leech is the subsequent profuse bleeding from the wound. When the leech bites it pours in its saliva which contains an anti-clotting chemical thus preventing the blood from clotting and keeping it liquid inside the leech's body.

Making one meal last a year

The leech may take up to 20 minutes to fully engorge itself with blood, consuming as much as five times its own bodyweight. Medicinal leeches have been known to make this one meal last for a year although they probably do feed more often. The leech is capable of this because of its crop which is able to distend enormously. In fact, the digestive part of its stomach is very small, the bulk being used for storage. The fully engorged leech is a singularly ugly creature but it is thus well adapted to its existence in the wild where its next meal is entirely in the lap of chance.

If you discover a leech attached to you, do not, if possible pull it off. A lighted match or cigarette will induce it to let go. After removing the leech allow some bleeding from the wound and then wash it with a strong antiseptic to prevent infection.

Not all leeches feed on mammals' blood. Most small leeches found in ponds and creeks feed on small invertebrates such as worms, snails or insect larvae. They either suck their body fluid or swallow them whole.

Suckers at both ends

The leech has a soft, annulated body, usually with no external projections. At the posterior end it has a noticeable circular sucker and a less noticeable smaller one around the mouth. They also have eyes but these are very primitive structures, consisting of a deep pigment cup in which lie a series of light-receptor cells. They do have other sensory structures in various parts of the skin which respond to touch, temperature, and also to various chemical stimuli.

Leeches proper fall into one of three orders. There are the Rhynchobdellae which have a proboscis turned back on itself; the Gnathobdellae which have jaws — these include the medicinal leech; and the Pharyngobdellae which have no jaws but a sucking pharynx.

Leeches move by swimming or crawling. To swim they move their bodies in a series of undulations. To crawl, they grip with their front sucker and then move or slide the back sucker up to meet it, forming the body into a loop. As they crawl, they usually wave their bodies about as if they were looking for something, responding to the stimuli around them.

Alternately female and male

Leeches are hermaphrodites, producing alternately eggs and sperm. Thus they do not fertilise themselves but function first as females and then as males. The sperm is implanted in the skin of the partner enclosed in spermatophores. When leeches are copulating they often remain entwined together for long periods. Long after copulation the fertilised eggs are laid within a cocoon. By the time the young leave the cocoon they are already miniature adults. ●

ANT I.R. McCann

CENTIPEDES

Often encountered in suburban gardens where it is sometimes disturbed under stones, logs or vegetation, the centipede can sometimes have a bite as strong as a wasp's, causing intense pain and swelling.

Centipedes have 100 feet? Wrong. Usually less — occasionally more. Centipedes are totally harmless benign creatures wriggling through a passive life? Wrong. They can bite and their bite has a lot of sting to it.

In 1976 in Kew, Victoria, a healthy, young man was bitten on the thumb. Some ten minutes later he collapsed and appeared to have stopped breathing. Fortunately he recovered on the way to the hospital — but a bite from a centipede is certainly not something to be treated lightly. The largest centipedes of northern Australia can produce very painful bites and the victim may be uncomfortable for days.

Centipede venom can cause anything from a temporary, sharp pain to an intense pain followed by blistering, swelling and inflammation. Most bites occur in suburban gardens. Centipedes will always try to escape rather than fight.

The centipede has a pair of fangs or in-curving nippers, at the base of which is a sac holding venom. There is also an appendage at the tail but this does not inject venom. The poison claws are used for capturing and killing prey but are usually not big enough to pierce human skin and the venom is not strong enough to hurt human beings. If bitten, cold cloths applied to the wound will relieve the pain.

Only one death has ever been recorded. A baby in the Philippines was bitten on the head by a very large specimen and died nine hours later. One Californian species, *Scolopendra heros*, leaves a red streak on the skin where it has walked. It makes tiny incisions with its numerous feet and if it is scared it drops poison, through its feet, into each incision causing intense irritation.

Centipedes eaten alive

In some countries centipedes are actually eaten. Some African tribes are supposed to devour a centipede alive when in a state of religious fervour and Indian children have apparently also been observed to pull huge centipedes from the ground and eat them. In Siam — now Thailand — centipedes were roasted and given to children as a cure for certain illnesses.

One hundred feet?

Centipedes are of the class Chilopoda — meaning clawfooted. Although the number of legs varies considerably, centipedes always have an odd number. The long, worm-like centipedes can have anything from 31 to 177 pairs of legs; another group, the Scolopendromorpha have 21 to 23 pairs of legs; and another only 15 pairs of legs.

With so many legs to operate, it might be thought that centipedes have difficulty in moving, as a well-known rhyme suggests:

'A centipede was happy quite
Until a toad in fun
Said 'Prey, which leg moves after which?'
This raised her doubts to such a pitch,
She fell exhausted in a ditch,
Not knowing how to run.'

However, their many pairs of legs enables them to choose and vary footholds, and in some species to move at quite a pace. Only one leg in eight is on the ground at any one time and the legs on each side are in opposite phase, thus staggering the points of support. A combination of walking movements in some parts of the body with muscular contractions and expansions in others results in thrust or pull being exerted by the parts of the body in which the legs are not used. When the centipede is in motion the legs swing out and around to compensate for their shortness.

The head of a centipede consists of a single lentil-shaped capsule. It is distinct from the body and bears a pair of antennae and three pairs of jaws. Opening into the mouth is a pair of salivary glands which secrete a fluid used for grooming the legs and other appendages. The body is divided into a number of similar segments, each of which has one pair of jointed walking legs, in contrast to the millipedes which have two pairs per segment. The first pair of legs are the poison fangs.

Most centipedes are about three to four centimetres in length but the Brazilian species, *Scolopendra gigantea*, has been known to reach 30.5 centimetres in length. This species can catch lizards, small birds and mice and was once observed devouring a live toad.

Centipedes are usually natural amber in colour, deepening into brown. However, some large species can be strikingly coloured, bright greens and blues contrasting with yellow. Some species are also luminescent at night, presumably as a type of warning colouration.

The house centipede

The cosmopolitan species, the house centipedes, *Scutigera forceps* or *S. coleoptrata*, is about five centimetres long and has a bite as strong as a wasp's. It is light brown in colour with three dark stripes and long legs which cause it to resemble a spider when it is running.

The eyes of the centipede are of little use. However, the body and legs are covered with small hairs which are connected with nerve fibres. These are sensitive to touch and moisture.

Centipedes are nocturnal creatures, living by day in damp, dark obscure places such as decomposing vegetation, under stones, logs or bark or in crevices in the soil. Many species are cave-dwellers and a few of the Geophilomorpha are marine.

Cockroaches devoured

The staple diet of centipedes is insects but they will also feed on worms and slugs and even the detestable cockroach though, unfortunately, one cockroach lasts a centipede a week. One large specimen of *Scolopendra gigas* from Trinidad was kept for over a year in the Insect House of the Zoological Society of London and fed on small mice which it devoured with alacrity. As already mentioned, *Scolopendra gigantea* will feed on lizards, small birds, mice and toads.

Centipedes hold prey in their mouths with their poison claws, while the mandibles and maxillae tear it to pieces. They also eat bees and wasps, cleverly catching them and then quickly dropping them until their venom has taken effect. They are primarily carnivorous but will occasionally feed on plants and may even damage crops if present in sufficient numbers.

In captivity, centipedes will also devour one another. However, the centipede must be a fairly distasteful morsel as spiders and other predatory animals will not touch them unless other food is scarce. The least fastidious scorpions will eat them. The Scutigera have a good trick: when caught, they leave a few legs behind waggling, to distract the predator's attention and make a break for it.

Sex without touch

Centipedes have two genital segments between the last leg-bearing segments, but they do not actually copulate. Fertilisation is by means of indirect sperm transfer. A blob of sperm is left on a specially constructed web and later picked up by the female. The sexes are very similar and sometimes a microscope is needed for humans to tell them apart. Fertilisation may take place as early as autumn, the eggs not being laid until spring or summer. ●

ANT — R&D Keller

Children are sometimes bitten while playing in sand (above), a favourite location for some centipedes.

Centipedes are usually a natural amber colour, deepening to brown and grow to a length of four centimetres. The female centipede (right) guards her nest of young until they are large enough to fend for themselves.

The hairy house centipede (above) is quite harmless to man and is often seen in tropical rainforest locations.

The centipede's many pairs of legs (below) enable it to change and vary its foothold and move at quite a pace.

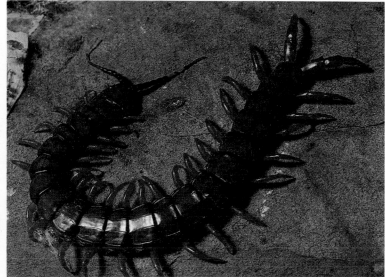

'The large and powerful claws grab and the mandibles and thorax section crush the victim.'

Scorpions are true predators they won't touch dead meat always preferring to grab live prey in their claws or deliver the deadly venom in their tail (right).

Scorpion with young on her back (below).

ANT A. Dennis

SCORPIONS

More of a danger to themselves than to humans

Fatalities due to scorpion bites are isolated in this country but even the limited symptoms of a scorpion attack are enough to make one wary. But in contrast to many other 'dangerous Australians' scorpions are more of a danger to themselves.

Scorpions have survived for some 400 million years, fossils having been found from the Silurian period, indicating that scorpions had been in the vanguard of life on dry land. They have been lumped together with spiders, mites and ticks in the class Arachnida; they belong to the genus Urodacus. There are only six families in existence today — but hundreds of varieties with very different characteristics and habits.

Three of the families are represented in Australia, mainly in desert areas — and none of them is classified as mortally dangerous. Only one death has been recorded, in Western Australia some years ago — contrast this with Mexico, for instance, where some 1000 people die annually as a result of scorpion bite.

Below: the tenacious claws and whip-like tail make the scorpion immediately recognisable.

Easily recognised

Scorpions can be easily recognised by their segmented bodies, well developed claws and the slender, curved tail — it's here that the venom is carried, in a reservoir, alongside a sharp barb which injects the toxic fluid into its victim.

Scorpions are true predators — they don't touch dead insects or animals; everything has to be alive, moving and fresh. The large and powerful claws grab and seize the prey and the mandibles and thorax section crush the victim to make it easier for the scorpion to suck out the flesh or juices. In most cases these methods are sufficient. Against larger or resisting prey, however, the scropion brings its venom into play: the tail flashes forward over the body and the deadly sting is delivered, preferably into a soft part of the victim, such as the abdomen.

The scorpion's venom — at least in Australia — hardly ever exceeds limited symptoms: swelling, intense pain and perhaps numbness.

Their favourite habitat is in high rainfall areas or the open, sandy expanses of the deserts. The desert species dig burrows for shelter. Most scorpions hunt at night — though they have poor vision. The number of eyes can vary from six to 12, according to the species but the scorpion prefers to rely on its sensory hairs arranged on its claws and other appendages to find its way to its meals.

One Australian species lives almost entirely off trapdoor spiders, common in desert areas. Whenever trapdoors tangle with scorpions, they invariably lose; the scorpion's venom hits first as the spider is held firmly in the grip of the scorpion's claws. Scorpions occasionally kill one of their own, too: in Western Australia scientists once observed a deadly duel in which both scorpions managed to score: one died within a day, the other 24 hours later.

Mate with grave suspicion

Mating is a perilous business as their instinct demands the release of venom almost on touch. Consequently, scorpions have evolved a mating technique without touching.

The lovers cautiously approach each other, then they clutch each others claws and leave their venomous tails carefully behind. After a brief courting dance, the male deposits on the ground his sperm and leads the female onto it; she scoops up the deposits and becomes impregnated. That done, the male makes a quick tactical retreat, letting the female go and backing away from the nuptial scene before he can be stung.

Young scorpions are born alive, emerging from the mother's body below the head: they are usually white, numbering about a dozen. Mother carries the newborn on her back until they are ready to fend for themselves. And, all being well, they will continue all this for another 400 million years. ●

Otto Rogge

MOSQUITOES

The low, irritating buzz of a mosquito is familiar to most Australians during the summer months. Like a dive bomber it homes in on its target, attacks with a well-armed proboscis and sucks blood from its victim. A harmless, red, itchy bite is the usual result but this can sometimes lead to a more serious illness.

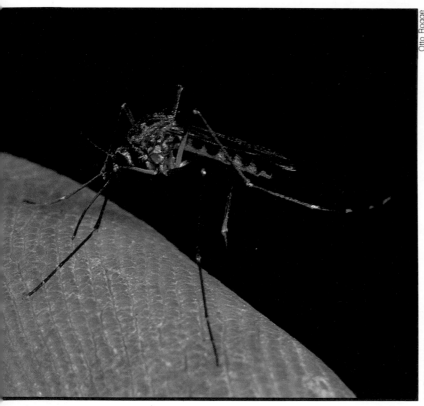

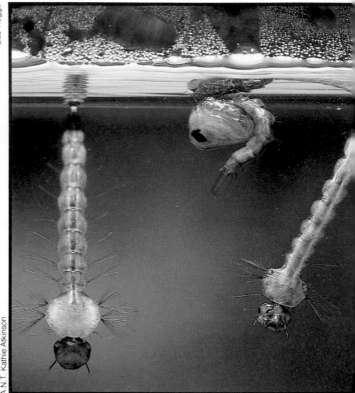

Otto Rogge

A.N.T. Kathie Atkinson

There are over 200 species of mosquitoes in Australia including three introduced species. Many of these insects seldom or never attack man and some are only occasional pests. Others are well-known as carriers of diseases such as malaria, filariasis, Murray Valley encephalitis, dengue fever and epidemic polyarthritis.

A number of exotic mosquitoes have been found on aircraft arriving from overseas. Fortunately, these specimens died when the aircraft were sprayed, illustrating the importance of this procedure as a protection against importing infective insects.

Like true flies, mosquitoes have one pair of wings and a body length of about six millimetres. They are characterised by scales along the veins of the wings and slender rear stalks or halteres which aid their balance during flight.

Piercing, sucking instrument

Mosquitoes' mouthparts are drawn out into slender stylets which, except when feeding, are enclosed in a sheath, forming a long proboscis which is specially adapted for piercing and sucking.

The familiar sting of the common household mosquito, as its stylets puncture the skin, usually alerts our attention to the presence of a mozzie. If left undisturbed, the insect then pumps up a quantity of blood and, at the same time, injects its own saliva into the bloodstream. The bump which appears on the skin is due to an allergic reaction to the mosquito's saliva.

A multitude of breeding grounds

Mosquitoes need water to breed. They are able to make use of almost any kind of water — clean, foul or brackish. Their favourite locations are brackish marshes, freshwater swamps, water in septic and rainwater tanks, roof gutters, flower

vases, water potplants, rock pools, discarded containers such as aluminium cans as well as temporary pools due to rain, floods or irrigation.

They breed throughout the country in all regions and climates but are more prevalent in the tropical north. Even in the arid, inland desert, eggs are laid during periods of rain and can remain dormant for months, hatching into larvae at the next rainfall.

After mating, the female finds suitable water and lays between 150 and 350 eggs. They adhere to each other to form an egg-raft which floats on the surface. One female may lay 5 or 6 such rafts in her short lifespan of a few weeks.

After a few days, the eggs hatch into larvae. If undisturbed the larvae swim down below the water with vigorous movements, then rise to the surface again. They moult, then change to pupae after a week or 10 days. The pupae, described as 'comma-shaped' hang down from the surface of the water and breathe through two respiratory trumpets. The pupal stage lasts only 3 to 5 days, then the adult emerges by splitting the dorsal skin and drawing itself out. The newly-emerged mosquito rests for a brief period before flying off.

Only female mosquitoes suck blood. Males feed on nectar and fruit juices. Blood seems to be a necessity if the female is to lay a large number of eggs. The dense swarm of mosquitoes often seen during summer at dusk are males, showing off their large, bushy antennae in an effort to attract females.

Keeping the mozzies down

In times past, the buzzing mosquito caused many people, especially those in the tropical north, to sleep under the protection of a gauze net. These days, fly screens on windows and doors and the handy insecticide spray has all but eliminated the house mosquito as a serious nuisance.

However, after periods of rain during the summer months, they breed quickly in the garden. They often remain in darkened parts of the house, attacking in the early morning and late afternoon, and feeding at night if there is no wind.

Populations can be kept down by attacking them during the water stage of their development. In permanent ponds, fish can be introduced to eat the larvae. Water tanks can be covered with gauze and all other containers which hold water should be drained or overturned.

Puddles and temporary pools should be covered with a thin film of kerosene; the immature mosquito must breathe air through tiny tubes in their tails and these are unable to penetrate kerosene.

Disease carriers

Excluding wars and accidents, it has been esti-

mated that the mosquito has been directly or indirectly responsible for 50 per cent of all human deaths since the Stone Age. It is therefore not surprising that the Guinness Book of Records lists it as the 'most dangerous insect in the world'.

Fortunately in Australia very few fatalities can be attributed to the mosquito. The common house mosquito, found everywhere except Tasmania, is the main carrier of filariasis, a disease which plays a significant role in dog heart-worm and fowl pox transmission.

The same mosquito that disperses yellow fever in Africa and South America carries dengue fever in Australia. It was once found as far south as the Hawkesbury River in New South Wales and Perth in Western Australia, but since World War II has been confined to tropical towns in Queensland where it remains common. It is a day-biting species that breeds in clean water sometimes containing a little vegetable matter.

The largest Australian mosquito, commonly known as the 'Scotch' or 'Hexham Grey', is a vicious biter and breeds in salt marshes in tropical and sub-tropical areas.

Another species, although rare, is found around Townsville and the northern areas of the Northern Territory and Western Australia. It is the most dangerous carrier of malaria in Australia and breeds in fresh or brackish ground pools and swamps in high rainfall regions.

Grassy areas inundated by floods and irrigation systems provide the main habitat of the mosquito known to be responsible for the Murray Valley encephalitis epidemics and the transmission of epidemic polyarthritis. If allowed to breed, this species can quickly build up huge populations. ●

The common house mosquito (far left) punctures the skin then uses a muscular pump to suck up a quantity of blood. It then injects its own saliva into the victim's bloodstream. The larvae and pupae (left) of a mosquito need water for their survival. Populations can be kept down if these watery breeding grounds are destroyed.

Not even the nocturnal Lesueur's frog (below) can escape the stinging bite of an attacking mosquito.

How A Mosquito Bites

The mosquito's proboscis is not the piercing organ. It is merely a hollow half-tube which holds the fine, sharp stylets and the sucking tube. What you feel when the mosquito bites, are the sharp stylets making the initial puncture. The sucking tube is then pushed into the skin. The hollow, sheathing half-tube then loops away so that it does not enter the skin but acts as a support and guide for the stylets. The mosquito then uses a muscular pump in its throat to pump up blood. At the same time, the insect injects its own saliva into the victim. This acts as an anticoagulant and lubricant, preventing the blood from clotting and allowing it to be sucked up easier.

Bay Picture Library

When coming in for the attack the horsefly will hover for sometime before piercing the skin of his victim with its proboscis.

THE BLOODSUCKING HORSEFLIES

In ancient times pastoral tribes would labouriously herd their stock across vast distances simply to avoid the ravenous bloodsucking habits of the broad, heavy female horsefly. Historical sources record that sheep were grazed by day and cattle by night in order to avoid the fly problem. Even today in some parts of Africa, tribes migrate hundreds of kilometres each year in order to save their cattle and camels from the onslaught of these pests.

> **'A grazing animal, in one day, can lose as much as one hundred cubic centimetres of blood.'**

It has been estimated that a single grazing animal, in one day, can lose as much as one hundred cubic centimetres of blood in satisfying the appetites of the horseflies. In addition to losing blood, they lose grazing time with a consequent drop in milk yield resulting in economic loss to the grazier.

Horseflies belong to the family Tabanidae, not all members of which are bloodsuckers. In the course of their evolution some species have lost the proboscis with which the bloodsucking variety pierce the skin of their victim. Interestingly, these species have declined on their purely carbohydrate diet whereas the bloodsuckers have flourished.

The true horsefly, also known as the March fly in Australia, is grouped into the large genus *Tabanus* which is found all over the world. They are thought to have arrived in Australia from the north along with the placental mammals. These biting flies range in size from 5 to 25 millimetres. Only the female horesfly sucks blood, the male surviving on a purely sugar diet of pollen and nectar.

Victims speckled with blood

When coming in for the attack, the horsefly will hover around the victim for some time before landing and piercing the skin with its needle-like proboscis. So intent are they on their prospective meal that they are quite easy to catch and kill during this hovering stage. A single fly can consume a considerable quantity of blood and also make a sizeable hole which usually oozes a drop of blood when the insect moves off. Attacked by many such flies the harassed animal is soon speckled with blood though the flies may carefully mop up every last drop.

Horesflies are not particular in their choice of victim. In addition to horses, they bite cattle, people and just about any vertebrate animal including such unlikely candidates as crocodiles, lizards and turtles. In Africa, even thick-skinned beasts such as elephants and hippopotami are not spared. The only apparent exemption is birds, probably because they are too fast for these slow-hovering creatures. It is not known however, whether flightless birds such as emus and cassowaries escape attack.

Although flies of this family in other parts of the world transmit diseases such as loiasis, none of the Australian species is known to transmit disease, nor do they occur in such vast numbers as in the northern hemisphere.

Mating and breeding

Hovering by the male appears to precede mating and males may hover in swarms to make themselves more conspicuous to females. This is often done above the treetops and may escape human notice. After a male is joined by a female, the pair fly off to rest, usually on a plant.

Spindle-shaped, horesfly eggs are deposited in masses, closely packed and stacked neatly on end, sometimes in two tiers. They are placed quite near the larval habitat, attached to plants in swamps and bogs, in mud, sand or rotting vegetation or beside rot holes in trees or logs.

Cannibalistic larvae

The larvae of the horsefly are elongate with formless, fleshy projections around each segment. Voracious carnivores, they eat small crustaceans, snails, worms, tadpoles, other insects and even each other. A number of *Tabanus* larvae kept together in a container will end up as one large larvae. Their sharp mandibles are also capable of piercing human skin, and they have been reported to suck blood from frogs, one toad even being injured after unwisely swallowing one.

Most larvae live for a year, but if not fully grown, a larvae may postpone its pupation for another year or even two.

Most pupae are found in drier soil, near the larval habitat. They usually emerge in the morning, en masse. Newly emerged flies are soft and sluggish for some time, unable to fly until their wings have hardened.

On emergence, the sexes seem to be present in roughly equal numbers, though once they have scattered in flight, the males are far less conspicuous than the females. ●

The march fly (below) or horsefly entered Australia from the north, being carried into the country on their hosts. Australian species do not transmit disease, but their sharp mandibles will pierce human skin.

Bay Picture Library

Will fight and bite to defend home

BULL AND JUMPING ANTS

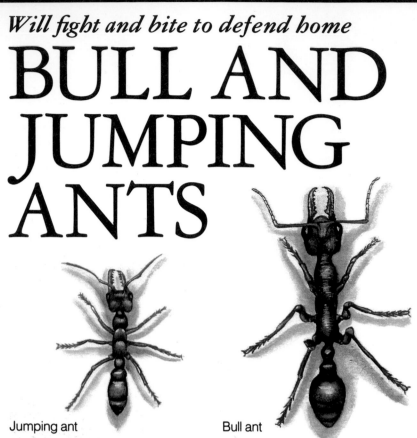

Jumping ant

Bull ant

Let's be grateful they never hold a family reunion: Australia has some 1100 species of ants, about ten per cent of the world ant population. And quite a few can deliver a very painful sting.

The bull ants — or bulldog ants — live up to their ominous name: they are not only unique to Australia but also the largest, with the Queensland species reaching 30 millimetres. At the same time, they are the most primitive of all ants. These, just like their close relatives, the jumper ants — or 'jumping jacks' — are highly aggressive and fiercely defend their territory even against an intruding man. They have powerful front jaws or mandibles with which they grab their victims, such as insects. With the prey firmly held, the ant curls up its body and thrusts a sharp sting into its victim. Jumping jacks can do even better: they can actually jump up to 20 centimetres and deliver their sting on landing.

Bull ants build underground nests and the pupae are enclosed in cocoons of papery brown silk. The adults feed on sugar and nectar while the larvae prefer insects.

The powerful mandibles on the bull ant are used to grab their prey.

ANT CA Henley

A.N.T MWF Tweedie

'After pupation comes the repayment: the young become workers.'

Bull ant dragging a dung pellet (left) back to the nest. Both species of ants live in a very organised society within the nest (below left); and (below) a bull ant nest is always to be avoided.

While bull ants must first climb onto their victim (bottom) the jumping ants literally jump to 'dinner'.

In common with most other species, bull ants and jumping ants live in a structured social order, forming male and female castes. The females are split into two groups: the fertile ones which establish the nest or colony and the infertile ones who become workers and soldiers.

Fertile queens start off life with wings — the others are wingless. Soldiers have large heads and the workers have strong jaws. Males have permanent wings, simple eyes and jaws with hardly any real function. In a colony, the queen is the largest by size, followed by the males, the soldiers and workers.

The courtship of ants has long fascinated scientists — and laymen, too. When it's time to establish a new colony, winged males and females swarm, mate in flight and then fall to the ground. The males die but the females only lose their wings and seek shelter, digging a small tunnel where the first eggs are laid and the larvae fed by the queen.

After pupation comes the repayment: the young become workers, find food and feed the queen, then excavate the chambers and passages of their nest either in the ground or in timber.

The honey bee, *Apis melifera*, is of great benefit to gardeners, but none too popular with those allergic to its sting.

BEES AND WASPS

*Fascinating species
with amazing
habits*

Who said bee stings give only temporary pain? About five thousand Australians will tell you otherwise. They are the unlucky people who are allergic to bee stings — and could well find their lives threatened by a sting from this common garden insect. Fewer people are allergic to wasp stings, but for those allergic to the venom, the results can be just as serious. And for those of us not allergic to either of these little stingers? The pain may be transitory, but it makes up for this in intensity.

Bees and wasps are closely allied, both belonging to the family Hymenoptera. In fact, bees are often considered to be wasps that have turned from a predatory existence to nectar and pollen feeding. Both are distinguished by having four wings, though the rear pair may be quite small, and a jointed body separating the thorax from the second part of the abdomen.

Wasps and bees both sting through a modification of the female egg laying organ, or ovipositor. The difference between them is that a wasp can inflict multiple stings because its sting is unbarbed, and can be withdrawn from its victim. Bees, however, have a barbed sting, much like a harpoon. Once a bee has stung, it attempts to pull itself free from its victim, which causes the poison glands attached to the sting to be torn out. The bee then dies from damage to its abdomen and venom glands.

Troublesome honey bee

Of the 3000 species of bee estimated to live in Australia, only one species causes considerable trouble to man — the European honey bee, *Apis melifera*. The large number of native bees are, for the most part, solitary creatures very similar to wasps in their habits. The social native bees, of the genus *Trigona*, are small dark stingless bees not dangerous to man. Mostly confined to northern Australia, they formed an important source of food for Aboriginals who savoured their sweet honey.

Bees are probably the most fascinating of insects and undoubtedly the most organised. Each colony contains a fertile female, or queen, infertile females, known as workers, and fertile males, drones. Each of these castes has its own specific roles to fulfil, and always places the good of the colony ahead of personal sacrifice and danger.

There is normally only one queen in a colony, along with up to 60 000 workers. The queen's task is to lay eggs almost continuously — up to 1500 a day — and to form new colonies when the time is right. The drones are responsible for fertilising the queen, but repeated impregnation with sperm is not necessary.

Busy working bees

Within a honey bee colony, most duties are carried out by the workers. The tasks that they perform seem to depend on the development of certain glands, as well as the requirements of the colony.

Apart from collecting pollen and nectar, and occasionally propolis and water, worker bees' duties include such things as cleaning cells, building cells and feeding larvae. Workers do not begin to forage for several weeks, although they do leave the nest after a few days to become orientated with their surroundings.

Drones are larger and stockier than worker bees. Their only function is to fertilise any young queen bee.

An Ichneumonid wasp (top) and the infamous European wasp (right). The latter is becoming a serious pest, and will stop at nothing to satisfy its appetite. Even steaks are utilised by this creature, which is particularly hard to brush off.

Bay Picture Library

ANT Otto Rogge

> **'Once they attach themselves to their food, they cannot be brushed off.'**

Scientists are fascinated by the complex social organisation of bees, as well as other species within the advanced order. The bodies of bees are adapted for the collection of nectar and pollen. To aid in this collection, bees have a body covering of plumose hairs, especially around the thorax, which trap pollen when the bee contacts a flower. On their third pair of legs bees also have a basket-like lobe for collecting and carrying pollen.

Another adaption peculiar to the bee is the proboscis, or special nectar lapping mouth, which is elongated and tube-like. Tongue length varies among the different species of bee, depending on the type of flower they visit.

Telltale food dance

The ability of bees to communicate their food source is one of the most remarkable feats within the insect world. When a worker bee returns from foraging he performs a 'dance' on the surface of the comb, which reveals not only the distance and position of the food source in relation to the hive entrance, but also its relation to the sun.

Many Australian crops such as tree fruits depend entirely on insect pollination to produce fruit, and many other crops and fruits are produced in greater abundance when pollinated by insects.

Another benefit that has arisen from bees is bee venom therapy, which has recently become well known. This form of therapy is used in some areas of alternative medicine to treat such conditions as rheumatism, muscular problems, arthritis and migraine. The patient is usually injected with bee venom and a number of other medicaments. In Great Britain, therapist Julia Owen applies a specially fed bee straight to the patients skin.

Wasps: solitary predators

Wasps too, can be of benefit to humans. They are natural predators, and many prey on insects which are considered pests to humans and to crops.

Wasps differ from bees in that they are all predatory. Their degree of social organisation varies, but most are solitary. Solitary wasps only meet long enough to mate, and the care of the larvae is totally up to the female. Solitary wasps often lay their eggs inside another insect which they have paralysed, ensuring a food supply for their larvae.

Social wasps live in colonies which usually have a queen, although they are not as highly specialised as the colonies of bees.

In Australia, the European wasp is becoming a great problem in some areas. The wasp is thought to have been introduced into Australia from New Zealand, where it is common. The numbers and range of these wasps has increased rapidly over the past few years, mainly because as an introduced species it has no natural enemy. In Australia, a nest which can contain up to 20 000 wasps can survive a winter — unlike most nests in Europe.

Europeans big eaters

Their numbers are further increasing because, unlike in a bee colony, there are thousands of queens in a colony of European wasps. These wasps are a problem because of their attraction to meat, sweets, pet food and garbage cans, which makes them great pests around homes.

European wasps are also voracious feeders. Once they attach themselves to their food, they cannot be brushed off. The State Agricultural Department is currently studying ways of decreasing the numbers of European wasps.

Most species of wasp and bee use their sting for defence, although some wasps do use it to paralyse prey. The venom in bee and wasp stings causes inflammation and irritation to human skin. This allergic reaction is caused by the histamine which is contained in wasp venom, and freed from human tissue by an enzyme contained in bee venom. ●

Bay Picture Library

CANE TOADS

Toads have always been associated in folklore with evil, witchcraft and sickness, but on June 22, 1935 when 102 cane toads arrived in Queensland, the organisers had only positive beneficial results in mind — to destroy the beetle causing extensive damage to sugar-cane crops. Unfortunately their good intentions backfired and Australia became home to another unwanted animal.

ANT — Peter Krauss

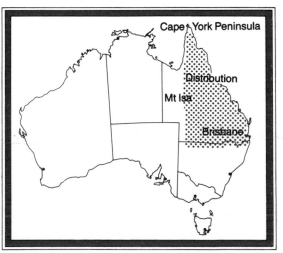

Not only did the cane toad prove to be ineffective against the sugar-cane beetle, the unseasonable warm, moist weather in July of that year provoked immediate prolific breeding activity and the toad soon turned from being a potential asset into an obnoxious pest.

At least three States in Australia have now declared the cane toad, *Bufo marinus*, a prohibited species or vermin and others are following suit. The cane toad which originally comes from Central and South America, certainly lives up to its pestulant reputation in looks. It is an extremely ugly creature, covered in wartlike growths and heavily built with short legs. It usually grows up to about 10 centimetres in size, but with abundant food and limited competition it has been known to reach 23 centimetres. Its colour varies from tan through to dull green.

Squirts of venom

On each side of its head behind the eyes it has a protuberant lump which is a paratoid gland carrying a highly venomous fluid. It can squirt this poison in jets up to a distance of one metre and usually aims at the eyes of its victim. It is highly venomous to small mammals and birds that unwittingly decide to make a meal of cane toad. Numerous birds, especially marsh birds, and other native animals die in this way, often only a few minutes after biting the toad. Snakes too, die shortly after eating one except, strangely enough, the keelback snake which seems to be able to survive this meal. It is not fatal to humans but a squirt of its venom can cause severe pain and all parts that come into contact with the toad should be washed immediately. Experiments have shown that the venom is not merely limited to the glands but can be secreted by a large area of the toad. So handling cane toads is definitely not recommended.

Devours precious dung beetles and honey bees

Quite apart from its nasty poisonous squirts, the toad has proved to be a severe nuisance in other areas. As well as eating the sugar-cane beetle it makes a meal out of the dung beetle, which was introduced to bury dung pats and so improve soil fertility. The toads approach fresh dung pats in the early evening and one individual can consume as many as 80 beetles at a sitting.

At the time of its introduction, Queensland bee producers expressed concern that the toad's appetite might extend to their precious honey bees. They were right and a toad happily consumes several dozen of these in a day, despite being stung.

The toad has also proved to be a pest in that it hangs around homes and swimming pools. Because, among other things it eats human faeces, it serves as a host for several unpleasant parasites, including roundworm.

Enemies of the toad

The toad is preyed on by a variety of animals, including rats, kites, the black snake and death adder, and the carnivorous plant, the bladderwort. Dead and moribund toads are eaten by crows and magpies without any ill effects. Crows eat them by putting them on their backs and inserting their bill into the mouth to remove their innards. Magpies make a hole in their abdomen. Prey birds are often responsible for the inadvertent spread of the toad. They carry it away from its established habitat to eat later, and the toad manages to escape.

The toad multiplies at an alarming rate. No native species ever achieves the densities of population that this creature does. The females are attracted by the vociferous croaking of the males gathered together in congregations of up to twelve toads. Mating takes place in the water. The female has been known to produce up to 35 000 eggs in a single spawn. The spawns are long strings of jelly-like substance containing the eggs, from which the tadpoles emerge after a period of 48 to 72 hours.

One major area of concern relating to the toad has been the problem of accidental release. In 1974 shipments of the toad destined for schools for dissection purposes were accidentally released at Darwin and Perth. On both occasions a case of virtual public alert was declared and fortunately almost all of the escapees are thought to have been recaught.

The sex change

One suggested method of combatting the accidental spread of the toad is to transport one sex only, the male. However the male cane toad is capable of undergoing a complete sex change into a fertile female. They have an incipient ovary but what exactly initiates the change is not yet known.

The cane toad has however, been extraordinarily useful to the medical and biological sciences. It has been used in experiments in laboratories since the late 1940s and for fifteen years, from 1950, it was used in determining human pregnancy. This method has now been superseded by biochemical procedures. As well as this, about 100 000 toads are used each year for dissection purposes in schools and universities.

'It can squirt this poison in jets up to a distance of one metre and usually aims at the eyes of its victim.'

Previous page: Although destructive, the cane toad has its uses; it has been used in laboratory experiments since the 1940s and was once used to determine human pregnancy.

An extremely ugly creature, the cane toad (opposite left) is covered in wartlike growths and is a host for several unpleasant parasites including roundworm.

Mating cane toads (opposite right). Females are attracted by croaking males and have been known to produce up to 35 000 eggs in a single spawn.

Behind the cane toad's eyes is a gland which carries a highly venomous fluid. When squirted, this poison effectively kills small mammals and birds. The white substance on the skin is the poison (right).

Bay Picture Library

Bay Picture Library

ANT C&D Frith

Marine Creatures

Looking for a sanctuary from all the snakes and spiders? Hoping to escape them by diving into the sea? Think again — here's a collection of 'nasties' from the waters around our coast that may make you a lot more amenable to the dangerous Australians of the land.

PORTUGUESE MAN-O-WAR

A hazard for all Australians who enjoy surfing, the Portuguese man-o-war or blue-bottle is some-times so plentiful in the summer months that certain beaches have to be closed. Washed up on the sand, they are often picked up by children who can receive a very painful sting.

Well known to most Australians who live near the coast, the Portuguese man-o-war often turns up during the summer months in shallow, inshore waters; groups of thousands have been observed floating off popular surfing beaches. When an inshore wind suddenly brings them into a crowd of surfers, there is a mass exodus from the water.

The Portuguese man-o-war, *Physalia physalis* commonly called blue-bottle in Australia, belongs to a group of invertebrate, jelly-like, marine animals noted for their ability to float and sting. They are widely distributed throughout the warmer seas of the world and in Australia range right around the coastline including Tasmania.

Translucent blue float

The blue-bottle gets its name from its body which consists of a gas-filled, bladder-like blue float. It may be as long as 30 centimetres and extend 15 centimetres above the water. The float has a crest which is used as a sail to propel the blue-bottle across the surface of the water.

Beneath the float are clusters of polyps from which hang long tentacles which bear nematocysts or stinging cells capable of paralysing small fish and other prey. The tentacles may be drawn up or extended over fairly long distances in their search for food and the stinging cells are capable of killing fishes up to 10 centimetres long.

The blue-bottle poison, like that of other jellyfish poisons is believed to be a labile protein. In experiments conducted on animals it caused failure of breathing and muscle weakness and the long tentacle which may grow to 10 metres is responsible for most of the stings.

Severe pain

Humans stung by a blue-bottle experience a sharp, severe pain and attempts to remove the tentacle may increase the number of stings. Single or multiple weals of different sizes will appear on the skin and occasionally they occur in a zigzag pattern when the tentacle attaches itself to the skin at certain points.

The sting of a blue-bottle can also cause a number of serious side effects including fever, shock and interference with heart and lung action. However, no known death has been reported.

The severe pain lasts about one to two hours. Where the victim has been extensively stung, the pain tends to spread sideways to involve surrounding joints, in the case of a limb, and may move around the trunk if the body has been stung. Severe pain may also occur in the lymph nodes when the venom reaches them.

In some cases, bleeding occurs at the site of the sting and occasionally ulcers and permanent scarring may result. There is also danger of serious damage to the cornea of the eye if the tentacles come into contact with the eye.

Pour on vinegar

As with all bites and stings, the victim should receive first aid immediately. Vinegar should be poured over the afflicted area and any adhering tentacles as soon as possible. Methylated spirits can also be used but vinegar has been found to be less painful to the victim. No attempt should be made to remove the tentacles before they have been inactivated by the vinegar.

Do no rub the sting or apply sand to the area. Any attempt to remove the tentacles should be carried out with a towel or other heavy cloth. An anaesthetic cream can then be applied to the affected area.

Usually the pain subsides within seven hours. However, if the reaction is severe the victim should be taken to a doctor or hospital and powerful pain-killers may be required; some persons have been known to develop severe allergic reactions to a blue-bottle sting.

Fortunately, most patrolled surfing beaches are well acquainted with blue-bottle victims and have first aid equipment within easy reach. ●

The translucent float or blue bottle acts as a sail to propel the organism across the water (above). The tentacles with their stinging cells can be extended long distances in search of food.

'Humans stung by a blue-bottle experience a sharp, severe pain and attempts to remove the tentacle may increase the number of stings.'

THE IRUKANDJI

The blue-bottle (bottom) gets its name from the gas-filled, bladder-like blue float which may grow as long as 30 centimetres.

Often seen washed up on sandy beaches (below), the blue-bottle is sometimes picked up by children who often receive a nasty sting.

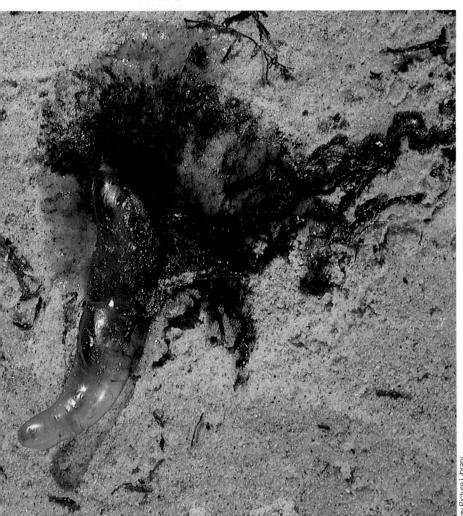

For many years, north Queensland bathers complained of a particular type of sting but were unable to explain what caused it. 'The irukandji is presented here as a 'dangerous Australian' for your information. Unfortunately *The Living Australia* was unable to obtain photographs of this species.

This stinging jellyfish type of organism is one of a number of stingers found in Australia's tropical waters. It ranges around two thirds of the coastline extending from Moreton Bay, Queensland into the Northern Territory and down the Western Australian coast to the Abrolhos Islands.

It is not as large or as dangerous as the box jellyfish or sea wasp but it has a similar, translucent, bell-shaped body and four tentacles which vary in length from a few centimetres to one metre. The tentacles are usually at least 40 times the length of the bell and may stretch up to 200 times longer. Tiny red dots which occur over the body and tentacles are the stinging capsules.

Aboriginal name

Those who were stung by this unknown organism gave the symptoms the name of irukandji stinging. Irukandji is the name of an Aboriginal tribe living near Cairns. It wasn't until 1961 that a Dr Soucott collected and identified the irukandji and gave it the scientific name of *Carukia barnesi*. Due to some difficulty in catching specimens of the irukandji, no laboratory tests have as yet been conducted on its venom.

Invisible attacker

In most cases the victim does not see the irukandji although the pain is felt within a few seconds of being stung. However, at this stage it is usually not severe enough for the victim to consider leaving the water.

During the first half hour some redness will occur around the area which has been stung and there may be slight swelling which usually goes down quite rapidly. On close examination, the tentacles may be found stuck to the body.

Pain and numbness

As late as two hours after being stung, other symptoms may develop; these usually include nausea, vomiting, sweating and agitation. Abdominal pain is sometimes caused by spasms of the muscles of the abdominal wall and cramps may occur in the muscles of the limbs.

Other common symptoms include numbness and tingling on the skin. Some victims have experienced pains around the larger joints, especially the shoulder and hip joints. Generally speaking the victim's temperature remains normal.

Avoid unpatrolled beaches

Although no deaths have been reported from the sting of the irukandji, they do pose a significant health problem to northern swimmers especially when a number of bathers are affected at the same time. Like many other stingers found in tropical regions, the irukandji can be avoided by not swimming in potentially dangerous waters and by heeding the advice of local surfing authorities. ●

Bay Picture Library

DEADLY STONEFISH

Few fish can match the sinister reputation of the stonefish but then not many species have as potent a venom as these grotesque gargoyles of tropical seas.

Stonefish form a family, Synanceiidae, within a much larger taxonomic group of venomous fishes that includes the red rock cod. The several species of stonefish, which frequent the Indo-Pacific region, all have in common a grisly appearance and the ability to inflict a lethal sting.

Australia's two representatives are largely restricted to the coastal waters of Queensland. *Synanceia verrucosa* is known only along the Great Barrier Reef, where it frequents the coral in shallow lagoons or tidal flats. *S. horrida* has a somewhat wider range, inhabiting mudflats and estuaries from Moreton Bay northwards but also as far south as the New South Wales border.

Alerted at the slightest disturbance

These fish are among the deadliest of all Australian animals. The venom is contained in twenty-six specialised glands lying below the skin on the creature's back. Ducts lead away from these glands up thirteen sharp spines — two venom sacs per spine — enclosed within fleshy sheaths. When the stonefish is not threatened the spines remain folded, but at the slightest disturbance they are immediately raised and protrude from their sheaths. The unfortu-

The grotesque stonefish (above) has wart-like bumps on its rough, mottled skin and eyes deeply set in bony hollows. Each of its 13 spines contains enough venom to kill a human being.

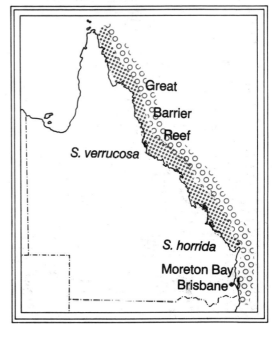

Australia's stonefish occurs only in northern, tropical waters.

Great Barrier Reef

S. verrucosa

S. horrida

Moreton Bay
Brisbane

Bay Picture Library

The favourite habitat of the stonefish is shallow water where there is a good mixture of coral and sand (left).

nate victim is punctured on contact and the venom is injected through a small opening at the tip of each spine.

Stonefish are indisputably ugly. In common with their relatives the scorpion-fish they have a bony ridged head and wavy fins but here ends the resemblance to any other living creature. The head and body of the stonefish are covered with lumps and fleshy growths and the eyes are deeply set in the bony hollows of the head. The large mouth is upturned and partly disguised by a notched fringe of skin. Most stonefish average about 30 centimetres in length but specimens nearly twice this size have been recorded. For those inclined to dally, the two Australian stonefishes can be told apart by the presence of a bony ridge above the eye, a larger number of pectoral fins and the whitish interior of the mouth in the reef species, *S. verrucosa.*

Their irregular shape and blotchy red-brown coloration afford stonefishes an extremely effective camouflage. This is enhanced by their ability to secrete a sticky fluid from the wart-like growths on the skin, which covers the body and to which cling algae and mud. Even small invertebrates such as sea anemones and hydras colonise the apparently inanimate object.

One might expect that the potential of the stonefish — each spine carrying enough venom to kill a human being — would be exploited by it to obtain food. This is not the case, however, and its deadly arsenal is utilised only as a means of defence. Its diet composed of small fish and crustaceans such as shrimps, a stonefish uses its large front fins to scoop out a depression in the sand or mud where it lies motionless waiting for its prey to draw near. Deceived by the convincing camouflage, passing victims are swallowed whole as the stonefish makes an unexpectedly energetic lurch forwards.

Unseen and unexpected

The combination of a largely immobile existence and remarkable camouflage is the cause of most stonefish stings inflicted on humans, as the fish is brushed against or stepped upon unknowingly. Shod feet have proved to be little protection, as stings have been recorded when the spines of the stonefish penetrated sandals and even rubber-soled shoes. Fishermen should be extremely wary of handling the stonefish even after it has been out of water for several hours: preferring shallow water, stonefish are often left exposed by the outgoing tide and have evolved the ability to survive beached for some time.

The effects of a stonefish sting are felt almost immediately. Pain at the site of the skin puncture

‘ . . . the potency of the venom is reduced with each succeeding sting. ’

Bay Picture Library

Ingeniously camouflaged by its rough, blotchy, red-brown colouration, the aptly-named stonefish is almost indistinguishable when lying motionless on the ocean floor.

Shrimps hovering around the seemingly inanimate stonefish soon become the main meal.

Bay Picture Library

increases so rapidly that the victim may lose consciousness. Swelling of the affected limb, irregular breathing and a reduction in blood pressure are common symptoms, and paralysis may occur. (These effects are attributed to the venom's ability to poison muscle tissue.) If death results, this is usually within six hours. Even if the injury is not fatal recovery is very slow, often taking six months or more. An antivenene now exists but it is of course difficult to ensure its availability on site. Placing the affected limb in reasonably hot water eases the pain considerably, as it renders the venom inert.

Definitely intrepid fishermen

Aboriginals of northern Australia were apparently well acquainted with stonefishes. The flesh formed part of the diet of coastal groups in Queensland, the creatures being speared by these intrepid fishermen. Mangrove sap was applied to relieve pain in the event of a wound. Models of the stonefish were fashioned from beeswax and used, in association with mimes depicting the effects of a sting, during initiation ceremonies.

On a consoling note, although perhaps cold comfort to those unfortunate to have encountered a stonefish, it is said that the potency of the venom is reduced with each succeeding sting. There have been few verified reports of this phenomenon and, presumably, even fewer volunteers to test it. ●

Bay Picture Library

THE BUTTERFLY COD

The butterfly cod,
Pterois volitans.

Bay Picture Library

A brilliantly-coloured butterfly
cod photographed on a reef
at Heron Island, Qld.

With its dazzling exhibition of long, feathery fins and a colourful body, the butterfly cod is one of Australia's most spectacular fish. It is also one of our venomous species; its 13 spines contain a toxin which can cause severe injury and pain.

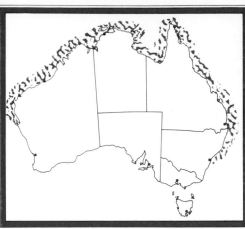

Bay Picture Library

Bay Picture Library

The spectacularly beautiful butterfly cod (above) has 13 stinging spines that can cause intense pain, skin discolouration and swelling. A bottom-dwelling species (top) the butterfly cod waits motionless until a small fish comes close enough for attack.

The beautiful but dangerous butterfly cod has a number of common names including zebra fish, fire cod, lion fish and red firefish. Although it has sometimes been found as far south as Perth and Sydney, the butterfly cod is more common in shallow waters around the coral reefs of northern, tropical waters.

The outstanding coloration of this fish gives it exceptional camouflage ability; its body has stripes of cream, yellow, pink, scarlet and warm brown. It grows to a length of 37 centimetres and its head bears a series of tassel-like appendages which gives it the appearance of a grotesque mask.

A spectacular sight

The spines and rays of the butterfly cod extend to exceptional lengths and well beyond the general level of fin membranes. With its fins extended and waving gently, the slow-moving butterfly cod has been described as one of the most spectacular sights in nature. It looks more like a

bundle of water-borne weed growth than the venomous fish that it is.

The butterfly cod usually rests motionless on the bottom until a small fish comes near. It then spreads its fins like a net to drive the fish into a suitable position for attack. The act of feeding is incredibly rapid. Its jaws are opened, the gill covers are flung wide and the floor of the mouth drops, causing a powerful water-jet which sweeps the unsuspecting prey into its mouth.

Popular aquarium exhibit

Although the fish has venomous spines, the flesh is non-toxic and good eating. However, most fishermen prefer not to tangle with the fish's dangerous appendages.

In recent years, the butterfly cod has become a popular aquarium fish with the result that more people have been stung by the spines. Often those setting up an aquarium are not warned of the fish's dangerous venom.

Underwater divers have observed that butterfly cod will often approach them, usually in pairs with their 13 stinging spines projected forward as a defence mechanism. When a person is stung, severe pain will occur instantly.

Intense pain and distress

The initial pain usually increases in severity for a number of minutes, often becoming so intense that the victim will weep and become greatly distressed. As a rule the pain subsides after a few hours but it may last several days. The puncture wound is generally numb and surrounded by a bluish discoloration of the skin and swelling. The more severe the sting, the more severe the general symptoms.

In some cases the lymph nodes draining the sting area become swollen and tender. Vomiting, fever and sweating sometimes occur but the most significant effect of the venom is the distress accompanied by severe pain which often appears out of proportion to the injury which has been inflicted.

Fatalities overseas

No deaths have been reported in Australia but the butterfly cod has been known to cause fatalities in other countries. As with other stinging fish, the victim should be taken to a medical practitioner as soon as possible where drug therapy will effectively treat the pain. In severe cases, local anaesthetic may be required.

If medical treatment is not immediately available, the wound should be bathed in warm water; many fish venoms are unstable in heat and this treatment will disperse the venom through the blood stream, decreasing the localised pain. Pressure techniques are not recommended over the stung area. In severe cases mouth-to-mouth resuscitation and cardiac massage may be required.

The stingrays are Australia's largest venomous fish. The sting from some species can cause excruciating pain and is sometimes lethal. However, the penetration of the poisonous spine is sometimes more dangerous than the venom, especially if the barb pierces a vital organ.

When he entered Botany Bay in 1770, Captain Cook made a note in his log book of sighting a number of stingrays weighing more than 100kg and so named the place 'Stingray Bay' which was later renamed Botany Bay.

However, thousands of years before Cook made his observations, the Aboriginals utilised the barbs of rays for spears which they used for fishing and combat.

Rays and their close relatives skates are plentiful in Australian waters; there are at least 50 species and they range right around the entire coastline. Broad, flattened fish with a thin tail, rays have some of the characteristics of sharks: open slit gills, spiracles or water inhalers, internal fertilisation and no bony skeleton, scales or swim bladder. Unlike sharks, their teeth are blunt which enables them to crush the shells of molluscs upon which they feed.

Sharp, serrated spines

Most rays have large, wing-like pectoral fins and a narrow, tapering tail which is armed with one or more serrated spines which can inflict painful, sometimes lethal wounds. Rays move by the undulation of their broad, pectoral fins although the large devil ray, *Manta alfredi* moves by flapping its fins like the wings of a bird and some rays use their tails as oars.

The manta or devil ray is the giant of the species and grows to a width of six metres and a weight of 1362kg. The devil ray takes its name from the pair of fins or horns on either side of the mouth. In spite of its forbidding appearance, the devil ray is harmless and its tail is not even armed with a spike. Other species of harmless rays include the shovelnosed ray, the fiddler ray, so called because the pattern on its back resembles the markings of a violin, the brown stingray, the long-tailed ray and the rat-tailed ray.

Dangerous to handle

Particularly dangerous is the cowtail or fantail ray, *Dasyatis sephen* which grows to a width of 1.5 metres. It is gleaming black above and white below and the upper surface is covered

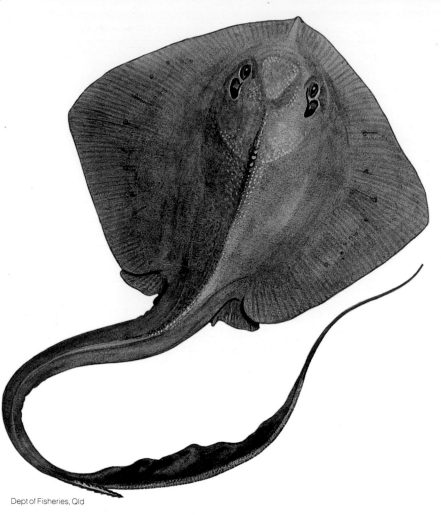

Dept of Fisheries, Qld

STINGRAYS

The cowtail or fantail ray (above) is a particularly dangerous species to handle because the barbs set in the tail can reach forward over the back and strike whoever is holding the ray.

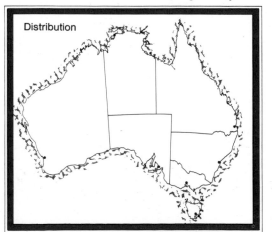

Distribution

'The cowtail ray is exceptionally dangerous to handle; it has barbs set in a long tail which can reach forward over its back to reach a wrist.'

with small granules. The cowtail ray is exceptionally dangerous to handle; it has barbs set in a long tail which can reach forward over its back to reach a wrist, even when the ray is held firmly with a finger in each of the spiracles.

The common stingaree or stingray, *Urolophus testaceus* is found in shallow estuarine waters as well as deep, offshore waters and is often taken in fishermen's nets. With its pale, sandy colour it is often difficult to see as it lies motionless on the bottom, often covered with a fine layer of sand.

The stingray prefers to evade an approaching wader but if it is trodden on will use one or more of the barbs in its tail in self defence.

The spotted eagle ray, *Aetobatus narinari* (also known as the flying ray and duckbill ray) is strikingly marked with scattered greyish and bluish spots and is often the cause of shark alarms at beaches where it is sometimes seen leaping clear of the water. Its long, tapering snout strongly resembles a duck's bill and the tail is unusually long and slender and carries from two to six barbed spines.

Other rays which carry spines dangerous enough to inflict injury include the blue spotted stingray, the blue spotted fantail ray or lagoon ray and the bull ray.

Electric shock of 200 volts

One of the most dangerous of the ray family, the electric ray, *Hypnos monopterygium* also known as cramp fish and numbfish, is capable of discharging an electric shock in excess of 200 volts.

The electric ray possesses a paired electric organ which lies behind the eyes. This structure is honeycomb-like in appearance and consists of a bank of hexagonal cells which effectively provide a positive pole on the upper surface of the body and a negative pole on the undersurface. An electric ray may deliver 50 successive charges within 10 minutes and each one is sufficiently intense to severely cramp an adult's muscles.

Sting is a defence mechanism

Stingrays usually feed on the bottom and often lie there motionless. If they are accidently trodden on or if someone swims low over them, they quickly defend themselves by a sudden vertical thrust of the tail. The spine then drives the venom into the victim.

There is a delicate skin over the stingray's spine and this is broken at the time of penetration; venom enters the wound by passing along the grooves which run along the spine. Because of the size of the spine, the injury can be extremely dangerous; a fatality occurred some years ago in Port Phillip Bay, Victoria when a man was stung in the heart. Underwater divers have also suffered the rupture of vital organs such as the liver and lungs when stung by a stingray.

Most common stings occur to the leg. Apart from the immediate danger of physical damage, complications may set in due to infection which could lead to death some days after the actual sting. Sometimes chronic infection may develop due to portions of the sting remaining in the wound. Medical attention should be sought immediately after being stung. ●

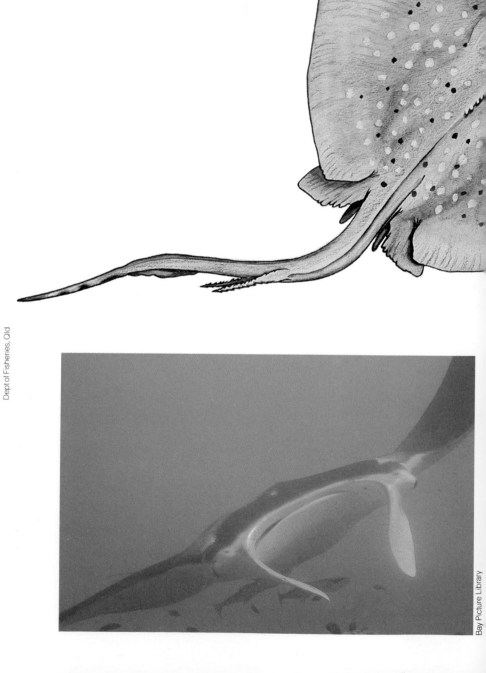

The spotted eagle ray (right) is strikingly marked with scattered greyish or bluish spots. The long, tapering snout is reminiscent of a duck's bill.

The blue-spotted stingray (far left) carries one or two spikes in its tail which should be avoided. The spots usually fade after death. The devil or manta ray (left) takes its name from its paired head fins or horns. These rays often leap clear of the water and in spite of their forbidding appearance are quite harmless.

The manta ray (left) swims close to the surface and its wing-tips often give the appearance of two sharks swimming side-by-side. The common stingray or stingaree (right) occurs on muddy and sandy flats where it is often taken in fishermen's nets.

> **' The electric ray is capable of discharging an electric shock in excess of 200 volts. '**

THE MOUTH ALMIGHTY

The red rock cod

Some fishermen refuse to pull the red rock cod into their boats because of the danger of handling this fish with its venomous spines.

Good to eat and often called the 'poor man's lobster', the red rock cod is often rejected by anglers due to its 13 venomous spines and needle-sharp fins which make it extremely dangerous to handle.

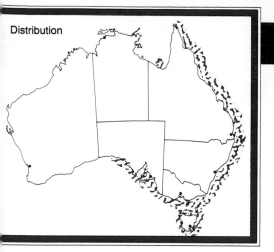

Distribution

'Although their delicious white flesh is excellent and tastes very similar to crab, many fishermen refuse to pull red rock cod into their boats. '

Bay Picture Library

The body colour of the red rock cod is mainly in shades of red and orange. It grows to a length of 40 centimetres.

Belonging to a group of scorpionfish of the family Scorpaenidae, the red rock cod is also known as the cardinal scorpionfish, the red scorpion cod and mouth almighty. They are quite common around the south-eastern parts of the Australian coastline and inhabit rocky, reef locations in water from 4 to 40 metres deep.

The red rock cod is a thick set fish and grows to a length of 40 centimetres. Brightly coloured mainly in shades of red and orange, it has the ability to camouflage itself by matching its body colour to its rock and weed environment. It feeds on crustaceans, molluscs and small fish and usually captures prey by a swift pounce, using its large, pectoral fins as auxiliary power units.

Like its close relative the stonefish, the red rock cod is armed with 13 venomous spines which can inflict a painful wound. In addition, its needle-sharp fins can also cause an injury which rather than a sting produces a burning sensation.

Delicious white flesh

The red rock cod is usually captured by anglers bottom fishing from the rocks over reefy areas or while fishing offshore reefs in deeper water; they are often taken accidentally by snapper fishermen. Although their delicious white flesh is excellent and tastes very similar to crab, many fishermen refuse to pull the red rock cod into their boats because of the danger in handling and filleting the fish.

Most stings and injury are incurred by anglers who are ignorant of the fish's venomous spines or who are not careful enough when handling the catch.

Medical attention required

A severe sting from a red rock cod requires medical attention. When a finger or hand has been stung, the victim will feel immediate pain which often spreads up the arm and covers the chest within an hour. Swelling of the affected limb develops within 10 minutes.

The victim may then be nauseated and experience hot and cold flushes. Breathing becomes difficult and is accompanied by chest pains. These alarming symptoms usually abate after two hours but the swelling may not subside for 48 hours. Even slight scratches from the poisonous spines are usually tender for days.

As a first aid measure, the wound should be bathed in water warm enough to be effective but not scald the skin. Many fish venoms are unstable in heat and the main aim of the warm water is to inactivate the venom under the skin. Also, heat increases the blood flow thus dispersing the venom through the blood stream. If concentration of the toxin is decreased, local affects are less severe.

Depending upon the severity of the sting, mouth-to-mouth resuscitation and cardiac massage may be required.

Bay Picture Library

The red rock cod inhabits shallow rock and reef locations where it cleverly camouflages its body colour to blend in with the environment.

A.N.T. Kathie Atkinson

Bony ridges across the cheeks, on top of the mouth and above the eyes are characteristic of the red rock cod.

CATFISH

Fishermen are the usual victims of the catfish. When struggling to gain freedom, the fish will use its sharp, venomous spines on anyone attempting to hold it. The toxin causes severe pain and often lasts as long as 24 hours.

Bay Picture Library

There are a number of catfish species in Australia which are either eel-tailed, blunt-tailed or fork-tailed. These are scaleless, inhabit both fresh and saltwater and take their name from the cat whiskers or barbels around the mouth area.

Catfish have a number of confusing names in various parts of Australia. For example, in New South Wales, South Australia and Western Australia, the estuary catfish is called the cobbler which is also the name given to a different species of stinging fish found in South Australia and Victoria. Other names for the catfish include eel-

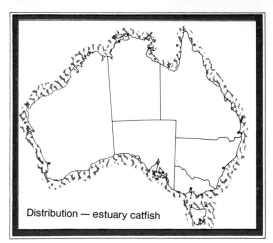

Distribution — estuary catfish

The eel-tailed catfish is a freshwater species found in the Murray-Darling River system and larger east coast rivers. It is a bottom-dweller and breeds well in dams. The catfish offers anglers good sport on light gear although extreme caution must be used when handling the fish (middle right). Its flavoursome, white flesh is best prepared by skinning and filleting.

The fork-tailed catfish found in saltwater reef and coastal areas is particularly venomous. Its sharp spines are capable of inflicting a painful wound which is often slow to heal.

The eel-tailed catfish is a mud-feeder or scavenger and spends most of its time foraging through organic debris on the bottom of rivers and estuaries.

Bay Picture Library.

tailed catfish and cattie.

Catfish have a wide range of habitat, from the quiet waters of estuaries, rivers and mudflats to coral reef waters at depths of 40 metres. They are bottom-dwellers and are more active at night. They are often captured in fishing nets where their removal often calls for pliers in order to cut the dangerous spines. The catfish diet includes worms, small shellfish and sea snails and they vary in length from five centimetres to one metre.

Good eating

Although the sharp spines of the catfish are highly venomous, the flesh is non-toxic and considered good eating. The freshwater species in particular is much sought after for its excellent flavour and is usually prepared for cooking by removing the skin.

Catfish have interesting mating characteristics. In one species the male uses its fins to scoop a hollow in the river bed and then builds a nest of pebbles. The female lays her eggs in the nest where they are guarded by the male.

In another species, the male actually carries the eggs in his mouth until they hatch and the young fishes retreat back into their father's mouth when danger threatens. The males do not eat while the are 'mouth brooding' the eggs.

Venomous spines

It is particularly dangerous to try and hold a catfish; three spines will spring out vertically and penetrate the holder's hand. There is one, long venomous spine on the back and two spines on the side or chest. The spines are extremely sharp and easily penetrate the skin. Catfish pose a particular threat to fishermen especially those fishing at night who may not be able to see what type of fish they have landed.

Severe pain

The venom glands of the catfish are located at the base of the spines. Venom enters the wound through a delicate duct which runs the length of the spine. Like other stinging fish, the toxin causes immediate severe pain. The severity is often far greater than expected, considering the size of the injury.

In most cases the pain lasts no more than a few hours but can persist as long as 24 hours. The sting of a cobbler or eel-tailed catfish in New South Wales has been known to hospitalise one unfortunate fisherman.

Medical treatment should be sought as soon as possible but as a first aid measure, the wound should be bathed in warm water to disperse the venom and a local anaesthetic cream applied to the affected area.

CONE SHELLS

Colourful, beautifully patterned and to all appearances perfectly harmless, some species of the cone shell are highly dangerous, possessing enough venom to kill a man.

So called because of their conical, cylindrical shape, cone shells are shellfish or marine snails which possess a toxin capable of inflicting serious injury to human beings and in some instances have caused death.

There are a wide variety of cone shells in Australia, most of which are found in northern, tropical waters. Some species have been found in temperate regions but these have been rare sightings.

The shell which is colourfully patterned is usually straight sided with a tapering body whorl, a low spire and a narrow aperture or opening into the first whorl of the shell.

Cone shells are bottom-dwelling creatures. During the day, they bury themselves in the sand and at night emerge to crawl around in search of food. Some species kill and eat small fish, others feed on worms, molluscs and other shells.

Poisonous dart

The victim of a cone shell is first speared and then paralysed by small teeth or harpoons which carry poison. These small harpoons have a num-

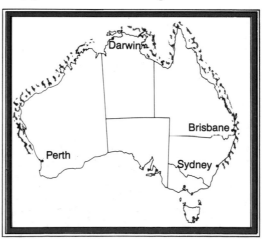

Textile cone, *Conus textile*, found in two metres of water off Tryon Island, Queensland. Insert: a detail shot of the harpoon of the striped cone, *Conus striatus*.

> **'The victim . . . is first speared and then paralysed.'**

Marbled cone shell, *Conus marmoreus* (right)

Neville Coleman

ber of barbs and are hollow. When the prey is sighted, the harpoon is pushed out like a dart and injected into the target.

Venom is then pumped into the prey which usually remains gripped by the cone shell although sometimes it may remain detached. In this manner, passing fish are speared, paralysed and then eaten.

Each cone shell possesses a number of harpoons which are about one centimetre in length and are made of a hard, bone-like substance. The principle effect is to cause paralysis of the major muscles of the body.

Fatality caused by geographer cone

The most dangerous species of cone shell is the geographer cone which has been known to cause at least one death in Australia. It is about 10 to 15 centimetres long and has banded brown to gold markings on a white background.

At least six other cone shells found in tropical waters are known to have sufficient venom to kill a man. The following shells are highly dangerous and are listed in order of their probably toxicity: the geographer cone, cloth of gold cone, tulip cone, marbled cone, court cone and pearled cone. Studies conducted on the striated cone suggest that it does not contain sufficient venom to be considered dangerous.

No guarantee of safety

Cone shells should not be handled except by those wearing heavy gloves. Those who inadvertently pick up one to examine it are in great danger if the shell is still occupied by the original inhabitant. Even holding one by the broad, blunt end may not guarantee safety because the snout with its poisonous dart can extend from the narrow end to near the base.

Impaled by one of these darts, a victim will first feel pain which soon gives way to numbness. If the dose of venom has been large, the next sensation will be tingling around the lips and mouth. Soon after this, breathing may be-

come difficult and the victim may lapse into a coma. Death will follow unless medical attention is sought.

In 1935 a young man picked up a live cone shell on Hayman Island. Stung on the hand, he felt no pain and the only visible evidence was a small puncture mark on the palm of his hand. After 10 minutes he complained of stiffness of the lips and after 20 minutes his sight was blurred. After one hour he was unconscious and in a deep coma and five hours after being stung he was dead. The shell was later identified as the highly toxic geographer cone which nowadays is rarely sighted.

First aid

Unfortunately no antivenene exists to combat the toxin of cone shells. A broad pressure bandage should be applied to the area which has been stung to stop the venom spreading to the vital parts of the body.

The victim should be kept still and medical attention sought immediately. Prolonged mouth-to-mouth resuscitation may be required if breathing becomes difficult. If a victim reaches modern intensive care treatment in a hospital early enough, it is possible to survive the paralysis which can often prove fatal. ●

Close-up of a cone shell (above) showing the fleshy interior concealed by the shell.

A top and bottom shot of the tulip cone, Conus tulipa, found on the Great Barrier Reef (below).

Striated cone shell is common in north Australian waters and though research suggests that this cone shell does not have enough venom to be dangerous to man, it should still be regarded as dangerous (below).

REPUTATIONS IN TATTERS

Setting the record straight on some of our misrepresented animals

One could be forgiven for assuming, after having read the preceding chapters, that we live in a land overrun by dangerous creatures. Certainly Australia may have more than its fair share of venomous animals — but there is no cause for alarm: the majority of animals, even those that look harmful, present no danger to man.

Some of these non-venomous creatures have an undeserved reputation; as a result, they are unmercifully shunned, swatted and trodden on whenever they cross our paths. Many of these creatures, if left to their own devices, will do us a great service by consuming unwanted pests.

Spiders are probably the most misrepresented of all Australian creatures. Because of the notoriety of the funnel-web and redback, all spiders are assumed to fall under an umbrella of 'nastiness'. In fact, the vast majority are completely harmless to man.

It may be unpleasant to walk into the

occasional spider's web, but the nuisance is far greater for a fly or mosquito that would otherwise have been seeking some human target.

Looking for meals

It is those spiders that innocently wander into homes that seem to cause the most distress. Known as hunting spiders because they do not build webs and wait for their prey, these spiders prefer to roam in search of a meal.

The most commonly encountered member of this group is the huntsman — often known, erroneously, as the tarantula. Scientifically there is no such thing as a tarantula. The name is a layman's term for any large, apparently hairy spider. The application of the name tarantula is an indication of the irrationality concerning spiders.

Huntsman spiders belong to the family Sparassidae. They all have eight eyes, arranged in two rows of four. Their wonderful vision equips them well for a predatory existence, as do their long legs.

Although they do not make webs, female huntsmans at least have not lost the ability to produce silk. They invariably enclose their eggs in a silk sac and guard it jealously until the young have hatched. The huntsman's flattened body enables it to move about in crevices that would severely restrict an average-sized spider. They are quite comfortable between rocks, or under loose bark. Wherever they choose to live they are skilled hunters.

Outside, the huntsman is well camouflaged against tree trunks or in leaf litter. Its predominantly brown colour blends in to its surroundings, allowing it to go unnoticed by prey that it may be stalking. But in a house, it stands out only too well against pale plaster walls, and usually ends its life sandwiched between the wall and a rolled-up newspaper.

Safe indoors

Such an end is hardly fitting for this spider. It will happily spend some time indoors, eating flies, mosquitoes, moths and a range of other pests.

A similar fate befalls many other spiders which would otherwise be engaged in eating insects. The only species other than the three mentioned in a previous chapter, that may cause genuine concern, is the black house spider, *Ixeuticus I. robustus.*

For all others a simple rule applies: leave them alone, and they will leave you alone. Whatever fears you may have are invariably without basis.

Remote danger

The same is true of snakes, but more so. Of the 140 odd species found in Australia, how many are genuinely dangerous to man? Probably about ten per cent. And, unless you happen to be bitten while in a particularly remote area, the chances

Bay Picture Library

of suffering a life threatening illness are negligible. No snakebite inflicted in Australia is likely to kill you within a few hours.

Yet despite this, stories abound of the fast-acting venom of some of our snakes. The death adder, for example, is supposed to cause death in its victims before they have walked the length of their shadows — unless, of course, they are bitten at night. Then, one assumes, death takes place before an owl has called twice, or the bats have flown back to their caves.

The simple fact is that most snakes are of no significant danger to man. It is also true, and worth noting here, that snakes are not slimy, but quite dry to touch. Nor is their tongue a stinging device, but rather a sensory organ. And a snake bite, along with bites from any other reptiles, will not leave an annually recurrent sore, like frostbite.

A female wolf spider, with her young on her back (opposite), and a huntsman spider (above). Both species are of no danger to man, yet are for some illogical reason shunned and swatted.

Deaf snakes

Other myths about snakes abound. They cannot be charmed by music, for they have no external ears and are largely insensitive to airborne sounds. (Snake charmers 'charm' their snakes with the movement of their instrument.) Hoop snakes, minute snakes and snakes which crack themselves in the air like whips do exist — but only in the imagination.

If you are still not convinced that snakes are not all dangerous, ponder this for a moment: what possible motivation could a snake have for attacking a human? Although they can swallow prey much larger than would be expected, they cannot swallow a human, even a small child. Therefore they are not interested in hunting humans. Nor are snakes inherently evil. 'Good' and 'evil' do not exist in the animal kingdom.

The only reason a snake has for biting a human is self-defence. If you see a snake and leave it alone, it will leave you alone. If you tread on it, or try to kill it, it will try to bite you. And can you blame it?

When a snake is forced to adopt an aggressive stance, it may be considered dangerous, but only if it is likely to inflict a serious injury. A vast number of snakes are unable to do this, either because they are non-venomous, or because their fangs cannot penetrate the human skin. It is these harmless snakes that are most certainly misrepresented.

Maligned pythons

The thirteen species of python found in Australia in particular suffer from an undeservedly fearsome reputation. None are poisonous and few are even aggressive when molested.

Pythons capture and consume their prey by two methods. They strike and hold the prey in their strong jaws, then throw several coils around the victim and commence squeezing it. This does not crush the victim to death, but suffocates it. Some smaller species may swallow their prey alive, dispensing with the constriction process.

The best-known pythons are the diamond and carpet pythons. They range from the Kimberleys of Western Australia, through the 'top end' of the Northern Territory, most of Queensland and New South Wales, along the Murray River to Southern Australia and Southwestern Australia.

The species is split into three sub-species: *Python spilotus spilotus*, the diamond python, *P. s. variegatus* and *P. s. imbricatus* the carpet pythons. They are all similar in body form, having large heads distinct from the neck, robust bodies and prehensile tails.

The dorsal coloration of *P. s. spilotus* is jet to olive black, with yellow or cream spots in the centre of the majority of scales. These spots form the diamond-shaped clusters that give this python its common name. The underside is

ANT Otto Rogge

Ivy Hansen

Pythons, such as this western children's (left) are often mistakenly seen as dangerous to man. Although some may threaten impressively (below) none are poisonous. Native bees, or sweat bees (bottom left), are quite stingless, and produce sweet, tasty honey. Our native rats, such as *Rattus assimilis* (bottom), are not the disease-carrying pests that many people assume.

cream to yellow with dark blotches.

Nocturnal species

In the carpet snakes, *P. s. variegatus* and *P. s. imbricatus*, the dorsal coloration is extremely variable. Usually it consists of a light to dark brown background with blotches and bands of paler colour, centred and edged with black. The central surface is cream or yellow with darker blotches. The maximum length of these pythons is 4.2 metres.

They are to be found in heavily timbered, coastal regions, and are a nocturnal, arboreal species. The keen observer may spot them in the early morning basking in the sun, but for the rest of the day they are secretive.

The green python, *Chondropython viridis*, is a nocturnal arboreal python whose emerald green scales camouflage it superbly. It feeds on small birds and mammals. Captive juveniles have been seen to use their tails as lures to attract prey.

One particularly beautiful python, the water python, *Liasis mackloti*, is normally found in close proximity to permanent water. The head and body are distinct, the body robust. The dorsal coloration is an iridescent olive green or olive brown and the belly is yellow or apricot. When disturbed it will not hesitate to take to the water. It has often been seen to eat waterbirds and their eggs. It apparently considers juvenile crocodiles a delicacy and will not refuse small mammals.

No lasting damage

Although a bite from a large python can be quite painful, and should be treated as any other injury, it is only a transitory pain with no long-term ill effects.

The same is true for the vast majority of Australian snakes, many of which are not even strong enough to bite through the human skin. But they are all efficient predators in their own right, and if given the opportunity, will aid in the control of many pests, such as mice and rats.

While on the subject of rats, is it true that they are all filthy disease carriers? Yes — if we are talking about the European black and brown rats; no, if we are talking about our own native rats. Unfortunately for the native rats, they look too much like the European species.

Except in the north of the continent, through the Northern Territory and Queensland, most native rats prefer to keep well clear of human habitation. And little wonder. The only things that would greet them in most homes are traps and baits.

Save the rats

There are 59 species of mouse and rat found in Australia, plus the introduced black rat and brown rat, but seven species are generally considered to be extinct. A further 12 species are known to be endangered and in need of immediate conservation measures.

Of these 52 remaining endemic species, only a handful are likely to be encountered by most urban Australians. They have not penetrated the urban environment, but may be seen in fringe areas where substantial tracts of native vegetation remain.

One species that may be seen along creeks, swamps and irrigation channels is the water-rat, *Hydromys chrysogaster*. This is a particularly attractive animal, well adapted to an aquatic life. Its sleek, lustrous fur is water repellent, and the webbed hind feet propel it swiftly through the water.

The water rat is found over most of Australia, avoiding only the dry inland areas. Although quite shy, it can be observed during the day feeding on aquatic insects, small fish and crustaceans, such as yabbies. Apparently it is none too popular in irrigation areas, as its tunnelling is said to weaken irrigation channels. But scientists point out that if it was removed from these areas, the subsequent population explosion of burrowing crustaceans that this rat feeds on would weaken the channels to a much greater extent.

Native bees

Because the native rats do not often extend into urban areas, their survival is rarely at stake through confusion with the European rats. This is also true of another creature, the much smaller, but equally benign, native bee.

Bees of the genus *Trigona* are, unlike their European counterparts, stingless. They are social bees, living in colonies of several thousand workers and the larger queen. The brood cells may be arranged in clusters, as in the subgenus *Pleibeia*, or in horizontal combs with the cells opening upwards, such as those of the subgenus *Tetragona*. The brood cells of the European honey bee, in contrast, are arranged vertically. The storage cells of *Trigona* bees, containing honey and pollen, are quite unlike the brood cells, and are large wax pots.

New nests are established without swarming. Workers gradually move nest-building materials to the new site, carry out construction, and stock the nest with provisions. When all is complete, a new queen goes there and establishes herself with a nucleus of workers.

Unfortunately for the thousands of Australians who are allergic to bee stings, there is little chance of the native bees ever superseding the European honey bee in commercial honey production. Although the native social bees do produce a sweet honey, favoured by the Aboriginals, it is not suitable for commercial development. So, even though you can't sample the fruits of this bee's labour, if one should land on you, don't be alarmed at the prospect of being stung.

Fearsome crocodiles

After sharks, crocodiles are probably one of the

ANT R & D Keller

Auscape Int. Jean-Paul Ferrero

most terrifying animals Australians are ever likely to encounter. No animal that can grow to ten metres in length, and call on such awesome power to overcome its prey, is ever likely to endear itself to the human population. But does the crocodile deserve to be feared? Well, if it didn't, it wouldn't be in the 'Top Ten' chapter earlier in this book. However, it is only the saltwater crocodile that has given some justification to its reputation. The freshwater crocodile is certainly not to be feared — except by fish.

Dr H. J. Frith, noted Australian conservationist, has summed up the reasons for the freshwater crocodile's misrepresentation:

'Both species are the victims of public apathy because of their appearance and revulsion arising from the incorrect notion that all crocodiles are man-eaters. They are destroyed by vandals with firearms, who feel that they are doing a good deed, whenever they are seen in a vulnerable position.'

Crocs protected

The freshwater crocodile, along with the saltwater species, has suffered terribly in the past from hunting. Thanks to legislation passed by the Western Australian, Northern Territory and Queensland governments, that finally became uniform in 1976, this hunting has largely ended. But the very nature of the 'top end' makes poaching a great problem; poachers are able to operate with few risks of prosecution.

With the gradual establishment of crocodile breeding parks, poaching will probably become less profitable. Efforts to eradicate poachers

could be hastened, however, if people altered their ways of thinking about crocodiles, and pressured authorities into action. As Dr Frith says, not all crocodiles are man-eaters; in fact very few look upon man as a food source. And no freshwater crocodiles are ever going to eat a person. They simply aren't big enough. But as with most wild animals, if you interfere with them, they will bite you. It's a very natural form of self defence.

Innocent gropers

Giant gropers, giant clams and giant squids have all been branded man-killers by legend — yet there is little evidence to support this. The Queensland groper *Promiscops lanceolatus*, is the largest known reef and estuary fish other than sharks in Australia. Gropers have been measured and recorded at lengths of up to three metres, and weighing over 300 kilograms. In Africa, specimens have been recorded weighing up to 600 kilograms.

The groper inhabits tropical and sub-tropical waters, tending to stay around anchorages, jetties and others areas which are good for scavenging. Because of their slow movement and bold nature, they became a target for spearfishermen and anglers, even though their meat is of poor eating quality. When their numbers became threatened, government legislation was introduced to limit the killing of the groper.

Although their reputation is bad, and the possibility of a groper harming a human does exist, there are few recorded cases of this actually happening. One authentic case of attack by a groper was when a groper bit, and severely lacerated the hand of a skindiver who was feeding it.

Giant clam

The giant clam is another misrepresented giant of the ocean. There are five species of giant clam which belong to the bivalve mollusc family Tridacnidae. They are abundant in shallow waters on coral reefs in the Indo-Pacific region, which includes Australia.

The largest of the species (*Tridacna gigas*) can grow to a width of up to 130 centimetres. One of the biggest ever recorded measured 114 by 74 centimetres and weighed 263 kilograms. It was found in 1917 on the Great Barrier Reef, and is now on display in the American Museum of Natural History, in New York. Not all giant clams deserve that title. Around the Great Barrier Reef lives a common species (*Tridacna maxima*) whose width averages about 20 centimetres.

Clam shells are oval-shaped with a strongly ridged exterior and fluted edges. The interior of the shell is pure white. The siphonal tissues of the clam, which line the outer valve lips, are brilliantly coloured, and make the giant clams the most conspicuous creatures on the coral reef. During early life, the muscular foot of the giant clam is used for locomotion. Eventually the clam attaches itself to one place, and often remains there for life.

Eating upside down

Giant clams have two widely separated syphons, through which a powerful jet of water is passed. This serves for both respiration and for feeding. The opening of the exhalant side is rounded and the inhalant side is fringed with tentacles, which helps the clam with feeding.

They differ from other molluscs in that they almost 'sunbake' to obtain some of their food, lying on their back with the siphonal tissue exposed to the sun. This tissue contains dense populations of unicellular algae which provides additional food for the giant clam through photosynthesis.

These cannot be absorbed through the digestive system, but rather are carried through the blood stream. This symbiotic relationship is interesting because the presence of the unicellular algae influences the form of the giant clam.

The unusual elongation of the siphonal tissue, as well as the upward display of the tissue area, gives a larger area on which light can shine. Within the exposed tissue are a number of structures which resemble lenses that serve to focus light deeper into the tissue.

Although there are no accurate reports of people being caught by giant clams, their reputation is extremely bad. Popular legends describe giant clams trapping men with an incredibly powerful, vice-like grip and eventually drowning them.

If a diver did become trapped within the

Freshwater crocodiles (above left) are not man-eaters, but they might give a healthy bite if they are annoyed. Ocean giants, like this big groper (above), are rarely aggressive, and will happily feed from the hand. Giant clams (left) present no danger to divers, as they close very slowly. In Australian waters, they are being ravaged by Taiwanese poachers, as in the photograph. Far greater patrols of our northern waters are needed before the clam population falls further.

Lynn Cropp

> **'There are no accurate reports of people being caught by giant clams.'**

valves of a giant clam, drowning would be certain unless the strong connecting muscle was severed. However, as the giant clam is both conspicuous and slow to close its valves, the danger is minimal.

Scandinavian legend

All squids are unusual creatures. In reality the giant squid is as fascinating as it is in Scandinavian legend, where it is known as the many-armed Kraken, a creature which drags small ships to the bottom of the ocean. The name squid applies to a number of different cephalopod molluscs, properly known as the Teuthoidia.

Like other cephalopods, squid have the ability to change their colour which ranges from brown, green or red to almost transparent. A gland in the mantle cavity also enables the squid to discharge a cloud of black 'ink', which confuses a would-be enemy.

Jet propulsion

The swimming mechanism of the squid is also unusual. Apart from their lateral fins which provide a means of fast movement and manoeuvre, squids are also 'jet propelled'. Water passes through a tube on the squid's body. It is then expulsed through another tube. The pressure of this water propels the squid.

Squids are fast and active swimmers, and often swim in large shoals. They are great hunters, and often outswim fish. They have two tentacles or arms that are much longer than their other eight. Often they are three times the length of the body and they are kept tucked away until the squid attacks a victim. When the squid does attack, these longer arms are shot out at great speed, dragging the victim back toward the mouth.

The giant squid was thought to be only a legend until the mid 1800s, when a large number of sightings were verified. The largest giant squid that has ever been recorded was found in Newfoundland in 1878. It has been calculated that it may have weighed up to 27 tonnes, with arms measuring up to about 11 metres.

At present no one knows the largest size that a giant squid could grow to. Many sperm whales have been found with giant squid arms in their stomachs, and tentacle marks encircling their entire bodies, where fights with giant squid have taken place. Although legends have called these, too, man-killers, there are very few records of a giant squid attacking men.

Attacks rare

The great fear of many swimmers is shark attack; since the release of the movie *Jaws*, many people have been, as the movie's promoters foresaw, afraid to go back into the water. The facts are, however, that shark attacks are particularly rare. Considering the extent to which our lives

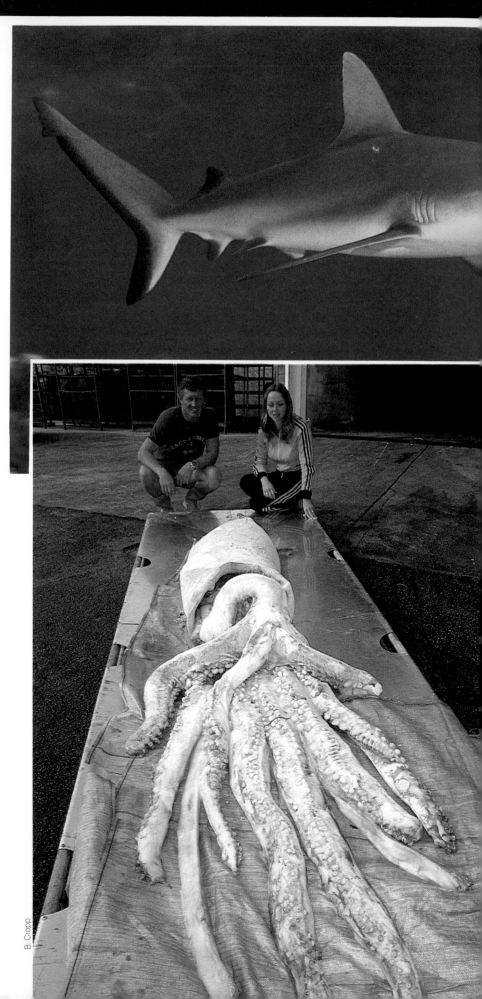

B. Cropp

The grey nurse shark (above) has been maligned for many years, but has never been involved in an attack in Australian waters. Giant squid certainly do exist (left), but it is unlikely they grow to the lengths reported in Scandanavian legends.

ANT R & V Taylor

'The flesh is probably eaten more often than is realised.'

revolve around the sea for six months of the year, it is surprising that more attacks do not occur.

Unlike the other dangerous Australians, sharks could have good reason for attacking humans. A snake may have little to gain from biting a person, as it cannot even begin to swallow anything so large — but a good-sized shark would have no trouble making a meal of a swimmer.

However, sharks do not seem to find humans all that tasty. Most shark attacks represent tasting lunges by the shark. Unsure of just what the object is, the shark moves in and has a test bite, then moves off dissatisfied. Unfortunately, when a shark makes a tasting lunge, it invariably does a good deal of damage.

There are, of course, certain species that are more likely to inflict a serious wound and some that are prepared to go all the way and finish off their selected meal. One species that will *not* do this is the grey nurse shark. Like most sharks, the grey nurse looks like a ferocious man-eater, but there is no evidence linking it to any Australian shark attack.

There are six species of grey nurse sharks which range throughout the temperate seas of the world but only two species in Australia; *Odontaspia taurus* which was previously *Carcharias arenarius* and *O. ferox* which was formerly *O. herbsti.*

The grey nurse is often confused with the sharp-toothed shark although the range of the two is very different. The grey nurse favours temperate waters while the sharp-toothed shark is a tropical species. Both these sharks have also been confused with the ferocious whaler which has endangered not only their reputation but their survival.

Fearsome appearance

The grey nurse shark has a heavy body, five gill openings and two dorsal fins. Under its pointed snout are forward-thrusting jaws, armed with an awesome array of long, curved teeth with small, thorn-like spikes on each side. However, these teeth are more suited to seizing and holding and are not as destructive as the slashing teeth of the tiger, great white and whaler sharks.

Grey nurses grow to a length of four metres and reach weights of 270 kilograms. Their colour is grey to brown on the upper side, shading to greyish-white below. The eyes are yellow with a black, slit-shaped pupil but without the third eyelid or nictitating membrane of other sharks.

No swim bladder

Like other sharks, the grey nurse has no swim bladder but unlike other sharks, it does not have to keep water flowing over its gills in order to breathe. It is thought that grey nurses retain air in their stomach and this allows them to remain

virtually motionless with their heads facing the current.

Grey nurse sharks are essentially fish eaters and often follow large schools of Australian salmon and mullet. Mostly they are found lazing on the bottom around reefy areas, often in quite large numbers. They are most common in Queensland, New South Wales, Victoria and South Australia.

Harmless unless provoked

Well-known underwater photographers Ron and Valerie Taylor, game fishermen and marine scientists support the view that grey nurse sharks are not dangerous unless provoked.

Fatal shark attacks in shallow Australian waters have often been attributed to them but in all cases, grey nurses have been blameless.

It is an extremely docile shark and when hooked puts up the worst effort of any shark species which is why it is no longer eligible for point scoring or records in game fishing.

However, tag and release programs are encouraged and it is hoped that information learned from tagging will reveal the shark's migration patterns, about which little is known. They do not appear to travel long distances north or south but often move from deep to shallow reefs.

When hooked, the grey nurse can be easily pulled to the surface on a handline, although often it will move a few metres, rest on the bottom and then become very hard to shift. Sports fishermen have described it as fighting like a bag of sand. The flesh is edible and is probably eaten more often than is realised.

Need for protection

Because of their slow-swimming habits and ability to remain motionless, grey nurse sharks fall easy victims to the spear fisherman's gun. As many as 30 sharks have been taken in one day's fishing. Because the gestation period is more than nine months and each female produces only two young, the grey nurse is particularly susceptible to fishing pressure.

Their numbers have now been reduced to the point where the species is in danger of extinction. Increased pressure on stocks has also come from offshore recreational fishermen, commercial fishermen and meshing.

It is essential to preserve this species in order to preserve the ecological balance of the ocean and to prevent the grey nurse's place in the ecological system being taken by a more active, dangerous predator.

Most people are familar with grey nurse sharks through a visit to a marine observatory or aquarium where they are often exhibited with other fish and where they seem to thrive. It is not unusual in these same surroundings to see a grey nurse shark being hand-fed by a 'brave' underwater diver.

FIRST AID

Your actions could save a life — possibly your own

Know-how gained at a good first aid course can save your life — this is the first thing to remember when dealing with bites, stings and similar types of injury. This chapter is intended as a guide to treatment only — it is by no means a course in itself. However, the points listed here may help to save a life — possibly your own — by outlining the main procedures to be followed in the event of envenomation.

The old methods of treating bites and stings are now discouraged by the medical profession as often they only increase and spread pain. Some are downright dangerous: the old idea of cutting the skin around a snakebite and sucking out the poison, then tying a tight tourniquet around the limb, has been replaced by the pressure/immobilisation method, a simple and extremely effective way of slowing the spread of poison through the body.

The pressure/immobilisation method involves placing a firm, but not tight, bandage along the entire limb that has been bitten or stung. This compresses the tissues, thus reducing the flow of venom along the limb. Quite often the venom will be trapped almost exactly where it entered the body. There are exceptions to the pressure/immobilisation method and these are discussed later in this chapter.

Land and sea snakes

In most cases it is obvious that the victim has been bitten; a strong emotional reaction is quite normal. It is important to first calm the victim, and give reassurance. Two fang marks are generally evident at the site of the bite, but in some cases only one mark will be present. Snakes often lose a fang, and it takes some time for a new fang to appear.

Other signs do not generally appear for 15 minutes to two hours after the bite. They include swelling of the bitten area, reddening and bruising, sweating, vomiting and difficulty in breathing. The victim may not even realise that he or she has been bitten; most snakes have very thin fangs, and a shallow bite may feel like no more than a slight pinprick.

The victim may also suffer from headache, double vision, drowsiness, nausea, pain in the chest or abdomen, loss of balance and diarrhoea.

The casualty should be kept calm and rested; all undue movement should be avoided. A pressure/immobilisation bandage should then be applied. If the bite is on a limb, as is usually the case, the bandage should start at the bite site, work down to the fingers or toes, then to the armpit or groin.

It may be necessary to improvise in the bandaging, using strips of clothing or pantyhose, but the first choice should always be bandages, either crepe or conforming, about 15 centimetres wide.

To immobilise the limb, a splint should be used. This is run along the affected limb, and bandaged to it, after the pressure bandages have been applied.

Having completed the pressure/immobilisation method, medical aid should be sought immediately. As any undue movement is to be avoided, it is better to send for an ambulance rather than attempt to transport the casualty. However, factors such as isolation and con-

First aid for snake bite involves bandaging the entire limb, after applying a broad pressure bandage to the bitten area.

Auscape Int. Jean-Paul Ferrero

The following diagrams show the recommended first aid procedure for snakebite of the lower limb.

1 Apply a broad pressure bandage over the bite site as soon as possible (don't take off jeans as the movement of doing so will assist venom to enter the blood stream. Keep the bitten leg still!)
2 The bandage should be as tight as you would apply to a sprained ankle.
3 Extend the bandages as high as possible.
4 Apply a splint to the leg.
5 Bandage it firmly to as much of the leg as possible.

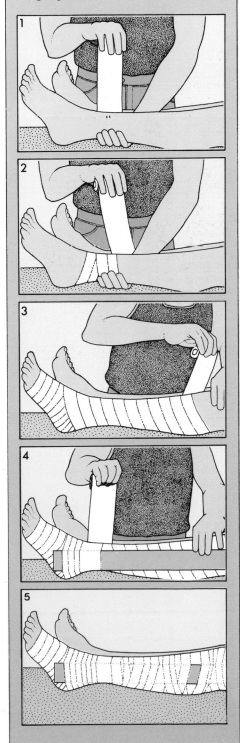

Bites on hand or forearm.

1 Bind to elbow with bandages.
2 Use splint to elbow.
3 Use sling.

If the bandages and splint have been applied correctly, they will be comfortable and may be left on for several hours.

They should not be taken off until the patient has reached medical care.

The doctor will decide when to remove the bandages.

If venom has been injected it will move into the blood stream very quickly when the bandages are removed. The doctor should leave them in position until he or she has assembled appropriate antivenom and drugs which may have to be used when the dressing and splint are removed.

tinuing danger will determine whether it is necessary to move the casualty. It is important that someone trained in artificial resuscitation stay with the casualty, as breathing difficulties, even complete breathing failure, may eventuate.

Venom detection kits are now available, and allow the identification of most snakebites from venom samples taken from the skin surrounding the bite. For this reason the affected area should not be washed. These kits also negate the need to capture the snake for identification, a practice that only results in undue risks and the possibility of multiple casualties.

It is reassuring to know that antivenom is available for all dangerous Australian snakes. If the pressure/immobilisation method is used, and the casualty receives medical treatment within a few hours of the bite, the chances of death are extremely slim.

Funnel-web spider

The funnel-web spider is the cause of much anxiety along the east coast of New South Wales. Many people still believe that a bite from this creature means death within minutes. This is quite wrong. Many people also believe that the larger female of the species is the more deadly; in fact it is the male that is the more dangerous. But as long as the pressure/immobilisation method is applied, in the same manner as for snakebites, the chances of death are very slight.

Unlike in snakebites, the casualty usually feels great pain at the site of the bite. Nausea and abdominal pain follow. The casualty will also experience difficulty in breathing, and a general weakness or numbness of the muscles.

The body also secretes heavily in several areas. Profuse sweating is usually obvious, along with excessive saliva production. Heavy coughing, producing secretions, is common.

Now that all major hospitals in 'funnel-web country' carry an effective antivenom, there is little risk of death resulting from a bite. Once the pressure/immobilisation method has been applied, medical aid should be sought immediately. A few days in hospital is the usual outcome, with no lasting damage.

The blue-ringed octopus (above), red-back spider (top right) and Sydney funnel-web (above right): all are creatures to avoid. Anne Richards (right) was fortunate enough to survive a box jellyfish attack; the scars she bears show the extent of the attack.

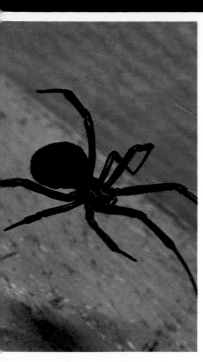

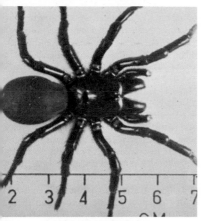

Blue-ringed octopus and cone shell

The symptoms of a bite from these two quite different creatures are almost identical, as is their treatment.

Because of the minute size of the injecting apparatus, the bite may go unnoticed, but the effects will be felt very quickly. After just a few minutes the lips and tongue become numb, followed by increasing difficulty in breathing and, soon after, complete failure of the breathing muscles.

Treatment for both these creatures is the same as for snakebite. It is essential that someone be ready to administer mouth to mouth resuscitation in the event of breathing failure. The pressure/immobilisation method will help, and is the only effective aid other than mouth to mouth that can be given.

Medical aid must be sought immediately; whenever possible, the casualty should be kept calm and still while waiting for help to arrive. They should not be left alone, as their survival may well depend on the continued, and correct application of mouth to mouth.

Stingrays

The treatment for stingray stings is much the same as for other stinging fish, but the pressure/immobilisation method may be applied.

Intense pain is immediately felt following a sting from this creature and, if the sting has occurred on the chest, breathing difficulties may be encountered.

First, gently extract the barb if it is embedded in the skin, then bathe the affected area in hot water, ensuring that it is not so hot as to scold the casualty. The pressure/immobilisation method may be used if general symptoms appear.

Medical help should be sought immediately, regardless of how well the victim feels. Even though they might have recovered fully from the effects of envenomation, further infection, leading to tetanus, is always a strong possibility. This holds for all bites and stings.

Ants, bees, wasps, scorpions and centipedes

Stings from these creatures are probably the most commonly encountered, and for all but those allergic to them, they are probably the least harmful. As in the case of the red-back spider, the pressure/immobilisation method only serves to increase and prolong the pain, and should only be used in cases of allergic reactions.

The first step is to remove the sting from the wound if it has been left behind, as usually happens with bee stings. Often the venom sac will still be attached to the sting, and pulling the sting out incorrectly will only serve to pump more venom into the body.

Bee stings, and any others that remain in the body, should be removed by scraping the sting sideways with either a fingernail or the side of a knife. Tweezers and similar grasping implements may cause further injection of venom.

It should not be necessary to seek urgent aid unless the casualty begins to show an allergic reaction.

If the casualty is known to be allergic to the sting, or begins to show a drastic reaction, the pressure/immobilisation method should be applied at once and medical aid sought.

In non-allergic cases, the casualty may gain some comfort from a cold compress applied to the skin after the sting has been removed and the surrounding area wiped clean.

Jellyfish

Initial first aid in the case of jellyfish stings is very much up to the casualty. The rule is: 'Don't panic'. If contact is made with a jellyfish in the water, gently back away from the reach of the tentacles. Attempts at brushing the tentacles off with the hands will only result in additional stinging.

If stung in deep water, some distance from shore, immediately call for help. Extensive stinging by species such as the box jellyfish may result in breathing difficulties within minutes, thus giving rise to the possibility of drowning. Anyone going to the aid of a casualty should take great care to avoid being stung themselves.

Box jellyfish

As the box jellyfish is rated as the most dangerous jellyfish, the treatment of its stings warrants detailed discussion.

The immediate sign of stinging is intense pain over the affected area. The extent of this area can be seen very quickly, as it will show definite

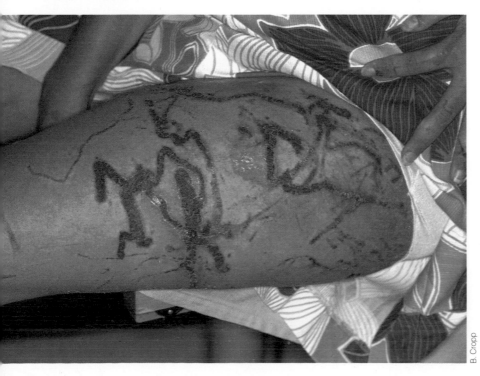

B. Cropp

B. Cropp

marks, usually red, along the line of the sting. The casualty will become irrational, and will experience difficulty in breathing. Breathing may stop at any time, necessitating mouth to mouth resuscitation.

When the casualty is removed from the water — taking care not to come into contact with the tentacles which may still be attached to the body — the affected area should be flooded with household vinegar. This will kill the tentacles within 30 seconds. They can then be removed, preferably with tweezers in case any live cells remain.

A firm compression bandage should then be applied over the stung area.

There is no substitute for vinegar; if this is not available, a compression bandage should be applied above the bitten area and the tentacles carefully removed with tweezers. Another compression bandage can then be applied over the affected area.

Medical aid is essential; wherever possible, keep the casualty calm and still while waiting for aid. An antivenom is available at most hospitals within the box jellyfish's range.

A competent person should be ready at all times to begin artificial resuscitation, and continue this until medical help arrives.

Other jellyfish

The signs of jellyfish stings vary somewhat according to the species responsible, but generally marks are evident at the site of the sting. The casualty may suffer from vomiting and pain in the affected area. Backache, chest and abdominal pain, nausea, lack of co-ordination and difficulty in breathing are also common signs of a sting.

Once again, the stung area should be flooded with vinegar or, failing this, the tentacles removed with tweezers. Ice water may be of help in reducing the pain, and can be applied liberally after the vinegar has had time to kill any live cells.

Medical aid should be sought, as breathing difficulties are often associated with jellyfish stings.

The old method of rubbing sand into a jellyfish sting should under no circumstances be used. All this does is activate more poison cells, thereby increasing the pain. The possibility also arises of being stung on the hand, as it rubs over the tentacles.

Exceptions to the pressure/immobilisation method

There are certain bites and stings where the pressure/immobilisation method is either impractical or undesirable. In these cases the following first aid methods should be applied.

Red-back spider bites

As the venom of the red-back spider moves very slowly, any attempt to restrict its progress would only serve to increase the associated pain.

No restrictive bandages should be applied.

The fangs of this spider are quite small and its bite may go unnoticed, but often a sharp pinprick will be felt. This is followed by pain at the site of the bite, leading to more general pain. Other symptoms include nausea, dizziness and partial loss of muscle control.

Sweating occurs in varying degrees, and is sometimes apparent around the site of the bite. Swelling of the affected area is common, as is a quickening of the heartbeat.

As with all other bites and stings, the victim should be kept calm and reassured. The only first aid recommended is to apply a cold compress to the wound; this may take the form of iced water in a plastic bag. The wound should under no circumstances be frozen. Where possible, take the spider along to the hospital for positive identification. Medical aid should be sought immediately. Most hospitals carry an effective antivenom for this spider.

Ticks

The signs of tick bites are often slow to emerge, and the casualty may not even be aware of the tick's presence. An unengorged tick is very small, and may go unnoticed in a body crevice or in the ear. The later signs of a tick's presence are a general weakness of the face and eyelids leading to weakness in the upper limbs and difficulty in breathing.

If the tick is in an accessible place, it should be killed with a drop of kerosene or mineral turpentine and then removed. If it is in an ear, medical aid should be sought, as its removal may be difficult.

When removing the tick, care should be taken to avoid grasping its body, as this may introduce more poison into the casualty. It is also important to remove the whole tick — the mouth parts, imbedded under the skin, should not be left behind.

Grasp the tick firmly with a pair of sharp pointed scissors or tweezers and gently lever it outwards. The lifting implement should be used as close to the skin as possible to avoid squeezing its body, and must not be used so firmly that the tick is broken in half, leaving behind the mouth parts.

In the case of small children or elderly people, medical aid should be sought. Such casualties generally have a decreased resistance to poisons of all types, and the effects of poisoning may be multiplied.

The casualty will generally start improving a few hours after the tick has been removed, but if this does not happen medical aid should be sought. There may be other ticks concealed on the body, so a search should be made for these.

Stinging fish

There are many species of poisonous fish potentially dangerous to man. Even those that don't

Lynn Cropp

A box jellyfish claims another victim (far left), this time a pilchard. Lifesavers along the northern coastline have developed a unique way of combatting this deadly creature — they don pantyhose (above). By covering their entire bodies, they are able to safely enter the water. An unengorged tick (left).

The tiger shark is a fairly common species on reefs around the Australian coast.

possess a poison may be dangerous since a wound inflicted by their spines can become infected.

Most stings are felt immediately, being characterised by a sharp and intense pain at the wound site, usually the feet. This then spreads along the entire limb. Many of the additional symptoms, such as irrationality and shock, are a direct result of the intense pain associated with these stings.

The stung area may show a blue coloration, and the casualty may also break into a sweat. In some cases the spine of the fish involved may have lodged in the skin.

Initial treatment is to place the stung area, be it foot or hand, into hot water. Fish venoms tend to be unstable under heat, and the hot water effectively inactivates and disperses the venom. The water should not be so hot that it scalds the casualty, and should be tested before immersing the affected area.

If the spine is still within the skin, it should be removed, along with any other foreign material. Medical aid should be sought immediately.

The casualty's breathing must be monitored closely and someone trained in artificial resuscitation should be on hand at all times. Mouth to mouth resuscitation may become necessary.

The pressure/immobilisation method should not be applied, as this will only increase the pain and result in localised tissue destruction.

An effective antivenom is available for the most dangerous of stinging fishes — the stonefish.

Sharks and crocodiles

Attacks by these creatures don't always mean instant death, but they are not to be taken lightly. At best they will result in the loss of a lot of blood; at worst, death or the loss of a limb may follow.

First aid starts with removing the casualty from the water, if he or she has been unable to do so already. Entering the water to rescue a shark attack casualty does not necessarily place the rescuer in great peril. Most sharks will leave once they have realised they are attacking a human. But if there are several sharks in the area, any blood in the water may trigger a feeding frenzy and further attacks.

It is largely up to the rescuer to assess the danger and make a quick decision. Obviously, if there is a boat nearby, and the casualty is some distance from the shore, it should be utilised. Great heroics may be applauded after the event, but a posthumous bravery medal does little to comfort grieving relatives.

In the event of shark and crocodile attacks, the victim must be removed from the water as soon as possible. Invariably, there will be bleeding, probably heavy, and this must be stemmed quickly. Two methods of stopping bleeding are prescribed: the first is for controlled bleeding, where damage has not been too great, and the second is for uncontrolled bleeding, where an artery has been severed, as in the case of amputations.

Direct pressure should be applied to the injured area in the case of controlled bleeding. This has the effect of stemming the blood flow long enough for a clot to form. Ideally, the pressure should be applied by a pad and bandage, but if these are not available, bare hands may be used.

The injured area should be kept still to allow the formation of a clot.

Wherever possible, the injured part should be raised. This is particularly useful if the legs are affected, but should not be done if they are broken.

If the first dressing has not proved effective, another dressing and pressure pad should be applied over the first. Do not remove the first dressing. Hand pressure may need to be applied, and may need to be continued.

In extreme cases, direct finger pressure may be necessary, even resorting to pinching the sides of the wound together. Such measures may be effective in stemming the blood flow from a severed artery, but continued application is essential. The pressure should not be removed until medical aid becomes available.

Where uncontrolled bleeding is encountered a constrictive bandage may need to be applied. It should be remembered, however, that this is a last resort.

Constrictive bandages completely block the flow of blood to a limb, thereby resulting in tissue damage. Where a limb has been severed their use becomes essential, as they are the only means of stemming the blood flow.

Bandages about 7.5 centimetres wide and 75 centimetres long, or clothing torn into strips of a similar size, are bound around the injured limb above the elbow or knee. These must be bound firmly.

The time of application should be noted, as medical aid will require this information. Aid should be sought quickly, as tissue damage occurs as long as the bandage is in place.

In populated areas, if someone is available, ensure that any other swimmers are notified of the attack and removed from the water. ●

'Fish venoms tend to be unstable under heat, and hot water effectively inactivates and disperses the venom.'